OCN Study Guide 2024-2025

Review Book With 330+
Practice Questions and Answer
Explanations for the ONCC
Oncology Certified Nurse Test.

HANLEY
TEST PREPARATION

Contents

Free Video Offer!

Thank you for purchasing from Hanley Test Preparation! We're honored to help you prepare for your exam. To show our appreciation, we're offering an Exclusive Test Tips Video.

This video includes multiple strategies that will make you successful on your big exam.

All we ask is that you email us your feedback and describe your experience with our product. Amazing, awful, or just so-so. We want to hear what you have to say!

To get your FREE VIDEO, just send us an email at bonusvideo@hanleytestprep.com with **Free Video** in the subject line and the following information in the body of the email:

- The name of the product you purchased
- Your product rating on a scale of 1-5, with 5 being the highest rating.
- Your feedback about the product.

If you have any questions or concerns, please don't hesitate to contact us at
support@hanleytestprep.com

Thanks again!

Introduction

Welcome to Oncology Nursing. Here, compassion meets expertise, as every day offers new challenges and opportunities to make a difference in the lives of cancer patients. If you are reading this book, congratulations - you have taken an important step on your journey toward becoming an Oncology Certified Nurse (OCN), marking an important milestone in your nursing career. This book is your trusted companion on this path, providing knowledge, guidance, and support toward this significant professional goal.

This book aims to give you the knowledge, strategies, and confidence needed to pass the OCN exam. Taking on such a daunting challenge can be both exciting and daunting; we understand some of the difficulties you might encounter on this journey. There is so much information out there, and knowing where to start studying may be hard. It serves as your trusted ally in this endeavor. It's intended to offer clarity and direction amidst an overwhelming sea of information, offering essential assistance along the way. Here's how it can assist:

- **Comprehensive Overview:** We've carefully distilled and condensed all of the key points necessary for success on the OCN exam into one concise document - no more sifting through tons of content; here you have it all at your fingertips.
- **Individualized Study Plan**: We know your time is valuable, so we provide a roadmap that allows you to effectively schedule your studies without guesswork about when or what to study. No more hassle.

- **Time-Saving:** Our study guide can save you time. By highlighting only the essential exam topics, our goal is to focus on where it counts most: your efforts where they matter most.

Imagine this: As an OCN-certified nurse, you stand at the forefront of oncology care. Your accomplishment opens doors for career growth, increased job opportunities and enhanced patient care. Passing the OCN exam is more than a personal milestone; it represents your dedication and hard work in oncology nursing.

This guide has been written by an experienced oncology nurse who understands first-hand the challenges you are up against. Their goal in creating this study guide was to impart knowledge and provide a study strategy that can increase your odds of success.

Their firsthand insight allows them to connect with your journey while tailoring the study guide specifically toward meeting your unique requirements as a future OCN.

They understand the importance of communicating complex information clearly and understandably while offering practical studying techniques. Their practical experience with oncology nursing, OCN certification, educational background and ability to create useful study material makes them the perfect guides on your journey toward OCN certification and career excellence as oncology nurses.

Your journey toward reaching your goal will become one step closer as you read these pages, absorb knowledge, and implement strategies provided here. When the OCN exam rolls around, you'll feel more prepared than ever.

Let this book serve as your source for empowerment, guidance and assurance that success in the OCN exam lies within reach. Embark on a rewarding journey together and make your OCN dream a reality.

Chapter One: The OCN Roadmap

"If you prepare yourself at every point as well as you can... you will be able to grasp the opportunity for broader experience when it appears."

– Eleanor Roosevelt

The OCN certification is a testament to a nurse's proficiency in oncology nursing and unwavering commitment to delivering top-notch cancer care to patients and their loved ones. Nurses who hold an OCN certification are acknowledged for their invaluable contributions to improving the quality of life for cancer patients.

While RN licensing demonstrates that you have the necessary entry-level knowledge for working in this field, it doesn't necessarily show your employer or patient your commitment to furthering your education and expanding your knowledge and skill. OCN certification is voluntary, assuring your employer and patients that you're committed to maintaining and acquiring specialty knowledge in oncology.

OCN certification provides comfort for your patients and rewards for you, the RN. While certification is voluntary, it may be required for you to advance in your career and open up new opportunities. All oncology nursing staff are certified as cancer specialists. They are not just medical professionals but also confidantes, comforters, and support systems for their patients and families.

Before you can take the OCN exam administered by the Oncology Nursing Certification Corporation, you'll need to complete continuing education in oncology nursing. Below are some of the eligibility criteria.

Eligibility Criteria

Acquiring your nursing degree is the first step toward becoming an oncology nurse.

Expertise in Oncology Nursing Certified: OCN nurses are experts in oncology nursing. This includes the care of cancer patients. They are well-versed in cancer types, treatment methods, symptom management and psychosocial aspects.

Patient-Centered Care: Certified OCN nurses are dedicated to compassionate patient-centered care. They have the skills to address the physical, emotional and informational requirements of cancer patients.

Quality of Care: OCN Certification demonstrates a nurse's commitment to high-quality healthcare. It shows their ability to use evidence-based practice and keep up with the latest advances in oncology.

Use these steps to acquire the education and experience necessary to become certified in this area of healthcare.

1. Earn Your Nursing Degree

Oncology nurses may have an associate's degree or a bachelor's in nursing. An associate degree provides faster entry into the field, while the curriculum of a bachelor's builds upon what was learned through an associate's.

The BSN program includes advanced nursing theory, pharmacology, nurse management, and research courses.

Even with an associate degree, you can still pursue a BSN. Many nurses enroll in accelerated courses after gaining clinical experience.

Your decision to pursue a nursing degree is ultimately your own, with no wrong choices available. Lifestyle, budget and availability should all be key considerations before making this important decision. Once registered as an RN, you can further your studies.

2. NCLEX-RN Nursing Exam: Passing the Exam

Before becoming a registered nurse, one must pass the National Council Licensure Examination for Registered Nursing (NCLEX RN). This exam is nationally recognized and serves to certify you.

Studying for the NCLEX can be hard, but it becomes easier with proper study plans and test plans. An NCLEX practice test allows you to assess your knowledge.

Your nursing degree should provide all the knowledge needed to pass the NCLEX, but further studying is also recommended to ensure all material is fully understood.

3. Gain Work Experience in Oncology

To pass the OCN certification exam, registered nurses (RNs) must have two years' worth of cancer care experience. Once you earn your RN license, begin searching for jobs as an oncology nurse - this may take at least a year of working as an RN before you are qualified enough for more complex duties within oncology care.

Once you have enough experience in a particular field, your understanding will vastly increase, and specialization can become a viable option. Once chosen, this specialization will determine which continuing education courses must be completed to become certified.

4. Consider Acquiring Specialized Qualifications

The ONCC offers four certifications specifically for Oncology Nurses:

- Oncology Certified Nurses (OCNs) offer specialization and experience to oncology-care nurses.
- Certified Pediatric Hematology Oncology Nurses (CPHONs) offer services specialized in pediatric oncology care for pediatric hematologic cancers.
- Certified Breast Cancer Nurses (CBCNs) offer their expertise.
- Blood and Marrow Transplant Nurse Certified.

Oncology-certified nurses can work with various patients. However, choosing a specialization area or patient population expands the potential even further.

Once you've met all eligibility requirements and passed your test, take the certification exam to maintain your certification.

5. Search for Oncology-Certified Nurse Jobs

Once you become an OCN, the possibilities open up before you. OCNs are highly in demand nationwide, and ShiftMed will match you to nursing jobs that fit your schedule and education requirements.

In summary, candidates must hold a valid, active, and unencumbered Registered Nurse license to take the OCN test from one or more US or Canadian states or territories. Furthermore, those taking the test must possess at least 12 months of experience working as licensed nurses within three years of applying to take part.

Before applying, you must have completed 1,000 hours of oncology nursing practice for adults within the last 2.5 years as an experienced licensed nurse in clinical, educational or administrative capacities. Your oncology CME requirements for the past three years must include 10 hours of continuing nursing education.

Exam Format

The Oncology Certified Nurse (OCN) exam assesses nurses' knowledge and ability in oncology nursing. The exam comprises:

Number of Questions: The OCN exam comprises 165 multiple-choice questions and 20 ungraded ones.

Time Limit: Candidates have up to 3.5 hours (210 minutes) to take and pass the examination.

Content Areas: The exam covers various content areas related to oncology nursing. Typical examples of such areas would include (Polit, & Beck, 2004):

- **Cancer Treatment Options:** Addresses all available cancer treatments, including surgery, chemotherapy, radiation therapy, immunotherapy, targeted therapy and hormonal therapy.
- **Symptom Management:** Covers concerns related to the assessment and management of symptoms commonly experienced by cancer patients, including pain, nausea, fatigue and mucositis.
- **Psychosocial Care:** Questions testing knowledge of psychosocial issues relevant to oncology, such as communication abilities, providing emotional support, and addressing end-of-life care.
- **Types of Cancers:** Concerns related to specific cancer types, their risk factors, early detection strategies and treatment modalities.
- **Cancer Survivorship:** Content focused on supporting cancer survivors, such as the long-term effects of treatment and survivorship care plans.

Exam Scoring: The OCN exam is scored from 0 to 500; its passing score is determined by the Oncology Nursing Certification Corporation (ONCC). Note that its passing score may differ slightly between administrations to account for slight variances in question difficulty.

Candidates typically receive their preliminary exam results shortly after taking an exam; however, these unofficial scores won't become official until several weeks post-exam date when an official score report will arrive via mail.

Please be aware that the OCN exam may change over time, so visiting the official ONCC website or contacting them directly for updated information regarding its format, content and eligibility criteria is advisable. In addition, consider investing in high-quality OCN review materials to prepare effectively.

Registering for the OCN:

Registering for the Oncology Certified Nurse (OCN) examination requires following several steps outlined by its certifying body, the ONCC. Since registration processes may have changed, please visit their website https://www.oncc.org/oncology-certified-nurse-ocn or contact them directly for accurate, up-to-date information on registration for OCN exams. Here is what to expect when taking one:

Eligibility Check:

Assure you meet the criteria for taking the OCN examination, including possessing an active Registered Nurse license and at least 12 months or 1,000 hours of Oncology Nursing experience within 30 months (often an average).

Create an ONCC Account:

Visit the ONCC website and create an account if needed; this account will allow you to register for exams and use other ONCC services.

Complete the Application:

Sign in to your ONCC account and complete an OCN exam application, providing information regarding your nursing education, professional experience, and continuing education activities.

Pay Exam Fees:

Pay the required exam fees, which vary based on exam type and/or ONCC website fees information. Payment can typically be made using credit/debit cards and other online payment methods such as PayPal.

Submit Required Documentation:

Depending on your eligibility and which program is right for you, documents such as proof of nursing license and details about oncology nursing experience should be provided accurately and promptly. Make sure all required documents are sent accurately.

Acquire Authorization to Test (ATT):

Once ONCC has processed and approved your application, they will issue you an Authorization to Test (ATT), including crucial information like your exam eligibility period and scheduling instructions. After receiving your authorization, schedule an examination.

Schedule Your Exam:

Use the information in your ATT to schedule an exam at a designated testing provider; OCN exams are generally administered through Prometric.

Prepare for the Exam:

To successfully prepare for an OCN certification exam, use the study materials and resources available. Enroll in review courses, utilize study guides, and practice answering sample questions.

Take an Exam:

On your scheduled examination date, arrive at the testing center with all required identification documents and other necessities to take and pass your exam within its allotted time limit.

Receive Exam Results:

Once your exam is over, preliminary results and score reports will be provided immediately; official ones and score reports should arrive shortly after that.

12-Week Study Plan

Preparing an organized 12-week study plan for the Oncology Certified Nurse (OCN) examination can be extremely helpful when studying for it. Below is a sample 12-week plan that sets weekly goals while covering key topics from ONCC's official outline:

Week 1-3: Care Continuum (19%)	
Week 1: *Health Promotion and Disease Prevention*	
Monday:	Intro to Health Promotion and Disease Prevention.
Tuesday:	Strategies for promoting patient health.
Wednesday:	Risk factors and preventive measures.
Thursday:	Patient education and health promotion.
Friday:	Review and practice questions on this topic.
Week 2: *Screening and Early Detection*	
Monday:	Principles of screening and early detection.
Tuesday:	Common screening methods in oncology.
Wednesday:	Early detection techniques.
Thursday:	The role of nurses in early detection.
Friday:	Review and practice questions on this topic.
Week 3: *Navigation and Coordination of Care, Advance Care Planning, Epidemiology*	
Monday:	Coordination of care in oncology.
Tuesday:	Advance care planning and decision-making.
Wednesday:	Epidemiology in oncology.
Thursday:	Putting it all together - Case studies.

| Friday: | Review and practice questions on these topics. |

Week 4-6: Oncology Nursing Practice (17%)

Week 4: Scientific Basis

Monday:	Cellular biology and cancer.
Tuesday:	Genetic factors in oncology.
Wednesday:	Mechanisms of cancer.
Thursday:	Genetic testing and counseling.
Friday:	Review and practice questions on this topic.

Week 5: Site-Specific Cancer Considerations

Monday:	Breast cancer nursing care.
Tuesday:	Lung cancer nursing care.
Wednesday:	Gastrointestinal cancer nursing care.
Thursday:	Hematologic cancer nursing care.
Friday:	Review and practice questions on these topics.

Week 6: Scope and Standards of Practice

Monday:	Professional responsibilities of oncology nurses.
Tuesday:	Ethical considerations in oncology nursing.
Wednesday:	Legal issues in oncology nursing.
Thursday:	Scope and standards of practice.
Friday:	Review and practice questions on this topic.

Week 7-9: Treatment Modalities (19%)

Week 7: Surgical and Procedural Interventions, Blood and Marrow Transplant

Monday:	Surgical interventions in cancer care.
Tuesday:	Procedural interventions in oncology.
Wednesday:	Blood and marrow transplantation.
Thursday:	Nursing care during transplant procedures.
Friday:	Review and practice questions on these topics.

Week 8: Radiation Therapy, Chemotherapy

Monday:	Principles of radiation therapy.
Tuesday:	Radiation therapy techniques.
Wednesday:	Principles of chemotherapy.
Thursday:	Chemotherapy administration and side effects.

Friday:	Review and practice questions on these topics.

Week 9: Biotherapy, Immunotherapy, Vascular Access Devices, Targeted Therapies

Monday:	Biotherapy and immunotherapy in cancer treatment.
Tuesday:	Vascular access devices and their care.
Wednesday:	Targeted therapies in oncology.
Thursday:	Nursing care for patients on targeted therapies.
Friday:	Review and practice questions on these topics.

Week 10-11: Symptom Management and Palliative Care (21%)

Week 10:
Etiology and Patterns of Symptoms, Anatomical and Surgical Alterations

Monday:	Understanding cancer-related symptoms.
Tuesday:	Anatomical and surgical alterations in cancer.
Wednesday:	Pharmacologic interventions for symptom management.
Thursday:	Complementary and integrative modalities in symptom management.
Friday:	Review and practice questions on these topics.

Week 11:
Palliative Care Considerations, Alterations in Functioning, Pain Management

Monday:	Palliative care principles.
Tuesday:	Addressing alterations in patient functioning.
Wednesday:	Effective pain management strategies.
Thursday:	Multidisciplinary approach in palliative care.
Friday:	Review and practice questions on these topics.

Week 12: Oncologic Emergencies (12%) and Practice Test 1

Week 12: Oncologic Emergencies and Psychosocial Dimensions of Care

Monday:	Disseminated intravascular coagulation (DIC), Syndrome of inappropriate antidiuretic hormone secretion (SIADH), Sepsis, Tumor lysis syndrome
Tuesday:	Hypersensitivity, Anaphylaxis, Hypercalcemia, Cardiac tamponade
Wednesday:	Spinal cord compression, Superior vena cava syndrome, Increased intracranial pressure, Obstructions
Thursday:	Pneumonitis, Extravasations, Adverse events related to the immune system, Venous thromboembolism.
Friday:	Take Practice Test 1 to assess your progress.

Week 13: Review and Assess Areas for Improvement.

Week 14: Practice Test 2 and Second Review

Within your final two weeks of study, step up your review efforts by focusing on areas in need of improvement as identified through Practice Test 1 results and taking Practice Test 2 to test yourself further and self-evaluate and adjust your study plan as necessary.

Consistency, active learning, and regular self-assessments are keys to your OCN exam success. Make changes as needed in your study plan in response to strengths and weaknesses identified during evaluation sessions as you stay committed to reaching your goals. Best wishes with your OCN journey.

Final Notes

The combination of a solid foundation of content knowledge and the confidence that comes from practicing your plan for applying that knowledge is the key to maximizing your performance on test day. As your foundation of content knowledge is built up and strengthened, you'll find that the strategies included in this chapter become more and more effective in helping you quickly sift through the distractions and traps of the test to isolate the correct answer.

Now that you're preparing to move forward into this book's test content chapters keep your goal in mind. As you read, think about how you will be able to apply this information on the test. If you've already seen sample questions for the test and you have an idea of the question format and style, try to come up with questions of your own that you can answer based on what you're reading. This will give you valuable practice applying your knowledge in the same ways you can expect to on test day. We will start this journey with Care Continuum.

Part 1: Exam Content Review

Chapter Two: Care Continuum

Chapter Two introduces you to an essential concept in oncology nursing: the care continuum. This chapter forms an invaluable basis for further investigation of oncology nursing practice and will form the cornerstone for subsequent, more in-depth topics.

Cancer remains a significant public health problem in the United States and worldwide. The American Cancer Society (ACS) annually estimates the number of new cancer cases and deaths expected in the United States in the current year. It provides evidence-based recommendations for prevention and early detection (ACS, 2015a).

The Cancer Facts & Figures documents, updated regularly, provide an epidemiologic report of cancer in the United States that offers insight into trends in cancer and its care (Brawley et al., 2011). Understanding its epidemiology is important to achieve the long-term public health goal of decreasing the morbidity and mortality associated with a cancer diagnosis.

Epidemiology studies how disease is distributed in a population, factors influencing its distribution, and trends over time. Although it often receives little attention in formal educational programs, understanding epidemiology is essential to comprehend cancer biology, identifying its risk factors, and developing prevention and treatment strategies. Epidemiologic studies encompass the basis of disease and the impacts of treatment, screening, and preventive measures on the natural history of the disease.

Types of Epidemiology

Two types of epidemiology are often applied in cancer: descriptive and analytic.

1. Descriptive Epidemiology

Provides information about disease occurrence in a population or its subgroups and trends in disease frequency over time. The information includes incidence and mortality rates and survival data. Data sources include death certificates, cancer registries, surveys, and population censuses (Greenlee et al., 2010).

Descriptive measures are useful for identifying populations and subgroups at high and low risk for disease and for monitoring time trends for specific diseases. They can be especially helpful in understanding the natural history of rare tumors. They provide the leads for analytic studies designed to investigate factors responsible for the disease profiles. Several common descriptive terms are used in epidemiology.

Incidence refers to the number of new cases of disease that occur during a specified period of time in a defined population at risk for the disease. Incidence rates also provide information about the risk of a disease or condition one has by virtue of being a member of a specified population. The ACS publishes projected incidence rates annually for common cancers in its annual Cancer Facts & Figures publication (ACS, 2015a).

Mortality Rates

The mortality rate is the number of persons who die of a particular cancer during a specified period. The ACS (2015a) estimated that approximately 589,430 Americans would die of cancer in 2015. This translates to about 1620 deaths per day.

Many epidemiologists consider the incidence and mortality rates together when making public health decisions. For example, breast cancer affects 1 in 8 women (i.e., 231,840 new cases) and results in 40,730 deaths annually (ACS, 2015a). It accounts for 29% of new cancer cases among women and 15% of deaths annually

(ACS, 2013a). In comparison, ovarian cancer affects approximately 1 in 66 women (21,290 new cases), resulting in 14,180 deaths annually (ACS, 2015a). It accounts for 3% of new cancer cases among women but 5% of deaths annually. Examination of these figures suggests either that ovarian cancer is diagnosed at a later stage on average than breast cancer, that treatment is less effective, or both.

Age-Specific Rates

Age-specific rates provide valuable insight and information about how disease risks vary among groups and populations. This often is extremely helpful when conveying information about risk to an individual. It also helps when considering recommendations for initiating screening. Screening recommendations consider that around 90% of breast cancer cases are diagnosed after age 40. For example, mammography is often recommended to begin at age 40 because most cases occur at this age or older (ACS, 2013a).

Health Promotion and Disease Prevention

Learn the basic principles of oncology nursing and health promotion, including strategies to promote patient health and preventive measures.

Screening and Early Detection:

This module explores early detection and screening as important topics in cancer care. With this information, you will discover ways to screen for cancer and detect it early. You will also learn about the important contribution that nurses make in diagnosing cancer early in the field of oncology.

Levels of Cancer Prevention

There are three levels of cancer prevention. **Primary prevention** refers to evading disease by immunization against childhood diseases, avoiding tobacco products, or reducing exposure to ultraviolet rays. Primary prevention measures may lower cancer risk but cannot prevent malignancy. Primary prevention measures include adopting a healthier lifestyle, using chemoprevention (e.g., tamoxifen to prevent breast cancer), and undergoing prophylactic surgery if there is a genetic susceptibility to cancer (e.g., bilateral mastectomies in a woman without a diagnosis of breast cancer who has a known mutation in the BRCA1 or BRCA2 gene). Oral contraceptives are recommended to aid in prevention of ovarian cancer families with Lynch syndrome, not genetically at risk for breast cancer.

More attention is being directed to primary prevention by reducing attributable risk. In addition to eliminating tobacco use to reduce smoking-related deaths, efforts are being targeted at human papillomavirus (HPV) vaccination, reduction of exposure to ultraviolet light, improved nutrition, and increased physical activity (ACS, 2013b). Unhealthy lifestyles, like poor diet, lack of physical activity, and obesity, contribute to 33% of the 572,000 cancer-related deaths annually. Another 33% is attributed to the use of tobacco products, according to Kushi et al. (2012). The combined use of alcohol and tobacco synergistically increases the risk of laryngeal cancer by about 50%. It is estimated that 80% of colon cancers can be prevented by dietary change.

Teaching about risk factors and the importance of testicular self-examination beginning in the teen years is the most important prevention method. The American Cancer Society recommends a shared-decision making conversation about prostate-specific antigen testing and digital rectal examination beginning at age 45 for men with a high risk of developing prostate cancer.

A woman's young age of a first sexual encounter (any age before 17 is significant) and multiple sex partners, drastically increases her risk of cervical cancer.

Sunscreen protects the skin from harmful ultraviolet (UV) radiation, which is one of the leading causes of skin cancer. Individuals should apply sunscreen with a high sun protection factor (SPF) to exposed skin areas, especially when spending time outdoors. Oncology nurses play a crucial role in promoting sun-safe behaviors and educating patients on the importance of sun protection as part of overall health promotion and disease prevention strategies.

Secondary prevention involves detecting and treating early-stage cancer in asymptomatic individuals.

Secondary cancer prevention forms include using a Papanicolaou (Pap) smear to detect cervical cancer, a mammogram to detect nonpalpable breast cancer, and a colonoscopy to remove polyps and detect early colon cancers. Cancer screening is aimed at asymptomatic persons to find the disease when it is most easily treated.

Screening tests seek to decrease the morbidity and mortality associated with cancer. Further diagnostic testing is necessary after a positive screening to confirm malignancy. This is the traditional definition of cancer screening. Some also consider screening for genetic or molecular markers that put the individual at high risk for cancer as a specialized form of cancer screening.

Tertiary prevention is managing an illness such as cancer to prevent progression, recurrence, or other complications. In cancer care, examples of tertiary prevention include monitoring for early signs of recurrence by measuring tumor markers or detecting second primary malignancies early in long-term survivors. An estimated 14.5 million persons are alive with a cancer diagnosis (ACS, 2015a). Because of this ever-growing population, there has been a push to develop cancer survivor care plans that include a component of tertiary prevention (Belansky & Mahon, 2012; Ligibel & Denlinger, 2013).

Medical History and Lifestyle Factors

Assessment of medical history and personal lifestyle factors that may increase cancer risk should be documented. The inventory can include information such as menstrual history, hormonal exposures, and exposure to carcinogens such as ultraviolet light or tobacco. Many risk factors are not within an individual's control (e.g., age at menarche) and are not amenable to primary prevention efforts. Some lifestyle factors are within the control of the individual and can be affected by providing education about primary prevention efforts.

After collecting all risk data, the clinician must assimilate the risk factors and inform the patient about their effect on each major cancer. Early onset of menstruation, never giving birth, and later onset of menopause are all factors that increase the risk of developing breast as well as endometrial cancer.

Risk communication should include discussing the presence of these risk factors as well as the risk of developing both cancers. Risk can be communicated to patients in several different formats. Often, it is best to explain the implications of a patient's medical history and lifestyle in terms of absolute risk, relative risk, and attributable risk.

For some cancers, it is possible to combine risk factors in well-tested models to calculate the risk of developing cancer at a specific age or over a lifetime. This is often done for breast, colon, and malignant melanoma.

A patient with ovarian cancer is at risk for the development of a secondary melanoma of the eye. Patients with Hodgkin lymphoma have an increased risk of secondary malignacy including leukemia and myelodysplastic syndrome, non-Hodgkin lymphoma, breast, lung and thyroid.

The Gail model is a tool created by scientists at the National Cancer Institute as well as the National Surgical Adjuvant Breast and the Bowel Project. It helps estimate the risk of a woman developing invasive breast cancer. The tool takes into account several risk factors, such as age at menarche, age at first live birth, number of previous breast biopsies, and number of first-degree relatives with breast cancer are taken into consideration. (Parmigiani et al., 2007).

Having a mother who was diagnosed with breast cancer before the age of 60 years has an associated relative risk of 2 to 4 times of those without this risk factor.

The Gail model estimates breast cancer risk and is most effectively used for women with a limited to moderate family history of breast cancer. It is often used to determine whether the patient should be enrolled in a chemoprevention trial or have breast magnetic resonance.

Patients who have previously had cancer are at increased risk of developing subsequent malignancies, with a higher likelihood of occurring in the same organ or site as the initial cancer. This phenomenon can be attributed to shared risk factors, genetic predisposition, or treatment-related factors. It is crucial to educate patients about this risk and emphasize the importance of continued surveillance and screening for early detection of subsequent malignancies. Although the risk may decrease over time for some cancers, the overall risk remains elevated compared to the general population.

Screening and Early Detection

Screening and early detection strategies are critical elements of oncology nursing practice, with screening used to detect cancer at its earliest, most treatable stages and help decrease mortality rates and enhance patient outcomes.

Early Diagnosis

Early diagnosis programs aim to decrease the number of late diagnoses. There are two main components to such programs:

1. Increased awareness of early cancer signs among doctors, nurses, other healthcare professionals, and the general public.

2. Improvement in access and affordability to diagnosis and treatment; enhanced referrals between primary level care and secondary and tertiary levels of care.

Early diagnosis is key when diagnosing skin, breast, cervix and mouth cancers and those affecting the colon, rectum and larynx or on other body parts.

Screening

"Screening" refers to simple tests used in healthy populations to detect those who may have the disease but have yet to experience symptoms. Mammography, clinical breast examination or pap smears can all be used for breast cancer screening purposes; cervical cancer screening options could include HPV testing, visual inspection or pap smears as well.

Screening programs should only be undertaken when their effectiveness has been established, and sufficient resources (personnel or equipment) are available to cover almost all of their target population. Screening programs must only be initiated when their efficacy has been verified, and sufficient resources (personnel and equipment) exist to reach all targeted groups.

Even when implemented correctly, screening programs can have undesirable consequences. These may include

- False positive screening tests that require further testing, invasive diagnostic procedures and patient anxiety;
- False-negative screening tests which provide false reassurance but delay presentation/diagnosis when symptoms do finally emerge; and
- Overdiagnosis/treatment of preclinical cancers that would never have caused symptoms nor presented serious risks is potentially harmful to patients, necessitating unnecessary procedures that endanger health.

These harms depend on the screening tests used, the population groups targeted for screening, and the quality of screening programs. Mass screening should only be recommended for colorectal, cervical, and breast cancers.

The WHO does not advise universal prostate cancer screening with PSA for men over a certain age due to the high harm/benefit rate associated with population-based PSA screening programs.

Frozen Sections

Frozen sections are useful in establishing and staging a tumor when a decision on the optimal type of surgical procedure is pending. They also provide information about the completeness of tumor removal post-surgically. They can elucidate the type of tissue involved so that it can be evaluated further, and they can aid in diagnosis through biopsy.

However, frozen sections are time-consuming and costly, so they should not be utilized when other options might be more complete or specific. A pathologist must also examine the sections in context because examining every portion of the tissue is virtually impossible. In addition, the use of freezing can damage tissue architecture and induce distortions.

Immunohistochemistry

Immunohistochemistry (IHC) is a technique in which tissue antigens on frozen tissue sections are identified. The antigens are detected by the use of specific antibodies coupled to either fluorescent compounds or pigmented entities, allowing the pathologist to view these interactions on a fluoroscope or through a microscope. There are also various methods of amplifying the interactions or enzymatically exposing masked antigens to aid in their visualization.

IHC distinguishes between benign and malignant (antigen-positive) processes and classifies the tumor type observed. It can also be a useful adjunct in determining the point of origin of the tumor and in identifying small areas that have metastasized. IHC can aid in the evaluation of the future aggressiveness of the tumor through the detection of characteristic nuclear antigens, and it can help predict therapeutic responses by identifying certain receptors, gene products, and proteins.

Biopsy Techniques

Surgical interventions in cancer are based partly on information gleaned from biopsies involving tissue removal for laboratory evaluation. At present, there are four ways that biopsies are obtained:

- Needle aspiration: The removal of tissue fragments through the use of a needle; this approach is usually highly specific and predictive if positive, but the sample size is typically too small to perform histological analysis.
- Needle core biopsy: Using a special needle to excise and retrieve a tissue section large enough for histological analysis.
- Incisional: Surgical removal of only a small portion of the tumor; this approach provides more information but requires meticulous technique to avoid sampling mistakes and the induction of tumor spread.
- Excisional: Complete excision of a suspected tumor area; used for relatively small tumors or when other methods are inconclusive. Most biopsies can be done with the patient receiving only local anesthesia, but general anesthesia may be required for excisional biopsies.

Fine Needle Aspiration

In fine needle aspiration (FNA), a small gauge needle is used to extract cells from a tissue area that might be malignant, and then the cells are observed microscopically. The procedure is usually done before surgery and is attempted in conjunction with other tools, such as X-rays and laboratory evaluations. FNA is relatively non-invasive and inexpensive. The utility of fine needle aspiration depends on the mass's nature because FNA can only broadly classify it and identify types of cells involved. Other issues, such as the architecture of the mass and its precise classification, are difficult to predict with FNA alone.

Cytogenetic Analysis

Collection Of Specimens

Cytogenetic analysis combines the use of cultured tissues and various precise methodologies in identifying chromosomal abnormalities. Tissue collection methods are designed to maximize the viability of the tumor cells ex vivo for analysis. Detailed patient information is sent to the laboratory along with the specimen, and the technician then chooses appropriate analysis techniques based on this information. Usually, a bone marrow aspirate (BMin sodium heparin is obtained for tumors of hematological origin; two to 3 milliliters of aspirate is generally sufficient. If it is impossible to obtain an adequate BMA (usually due to fibrotic tissue), peripheral blood samples or bone marrow biopsies may be taken instead. Other body fluids or tissues containing tumor cells may also be collected using the sterile technique for cytogenetic analysis.

Analysis Performed

Cytogenetic analysis is performed to look for chromosomal abnormalities during metaphase, the portion of mitosis where chromosomes align along an equatorial plane. Currently, the following types of analysis are done:

- Chromosome banding or karyotyping: Uses techniques to visualize the bands between A-T and G-C pairs to search for abnormalities, such as translocations, deletions, and breakpoints.
- Flow cytometry: Looks for ploidy. The term "ploidy" is used to describe an organism's chromosomal count (Crespel & Meynet, 2017).
- Fluorescence in situ hybridization (FISH): Uses fluorescently labeled sequences of DNA to probe for complementary strands in the sample (a variant called multicolor or M-FISH uses several different labels).
- Comparative genomic hybridization (CGH): Labeled tumor DNA is co-cultured with normal labeled reference DNA hybridized to standard metaphase chromosomes.

Types Of Changes Identified

Cytogenetic analysis can distinguish whether chromosomal aberrations involve the following:

- No loss of genetic content but only relocations of DNA that give rise to different gene products.
- Some deficit or gain relative to normal genetic material, such as deletions or duplications.
- Amplification of genetic regions.

Specific chromosomal abnormalities have been correlated with a variety of lymphoproliferative disorders and solid tumors. Any variation in the karyotype (ie., the standard size, shape, and number of chromosomes) can also provide information about the prognosis for the patient by assessing whether the aberration is seen in a single clone of cells or in conjunction with other abnormalities in subclones.

When confirming prostate cancer, a transrectal ultrasound (TRUS)-guided biopsy is considered the gold standard diagnostic measure. TRUS-guided biopsy allows for visualizing the prostate gland and guiding the biopsy needle to obtain tissue samples for examination.

Flow Cytometry

Flow cytometry is a method of analyzing populations of cells in suspension for various properties. The cells, such as tumor sample cells, are aspirated into the fluidic system of a machine called a flow cytometer. Here, the cells are mixed with a fluid that places them in suspension, creating a unidirectional or laminar flow.

As each cell flows past a laser sensor, photons emitted are picked up and intensified by photomultiplier tubes. Data is electronically converted into either histograms or dot plots that compare the characteristics of the cells in the population. In addition, fluorochromes are usually injected into the mixture to highlight further and identify the cell populations. A fluorochrome is a fluorescent dye, i.e., a substance that absorbs light at a particular wavelength but can emit it at more than one wavelength, such as fluorescein isothiocyanate (FITC).

Flow Cytometry For Acute Leukemia

Acute leukemia is one type of hematological neoplasia. Flow cytometry establishes the lineage or population from which the leukemia cells are derived, either myeloid or lymphoid. The most common approach is to isolate the blast cell population using a common leukocyte antigen called CD45 and then differentiate the cellular origin using other labeled antibodies.

Flow cytometry can find and count blasts, identify the phenotypes of the leukemic cells, and pinpoint molecular or cytogenetic changes. It is useful for detecting minimal residual disease (MRD) in the bone marrow. MRD is identified in flow cytometry by utilizing a panel of antibodies that target antigenic markers expressed in different patterns in leukemic and normal cells.

Flow Cytometry For Lymphoma And Other Lymphoproliferative Disorders

There is no universal gating marker for B-cell malignancies such as lymphoma, so the initial step in flow cytometric analysis of lymphoma tissues is segregating the malignant cells using a general B-cell antibody-like CD19 or CD20. The technique has limitations for lymphoma identification because these cells are difficult to bring into suspension, and fine-needle aspirates are often used. For lymphoma cases, tissue immunohistochemistry is often used in conjunction with cytometry.

On the other hand, chronic lymphoproliferative diseases are usually easily classified using flow cytometry. For example, B-lymphocytes found in individuals with chronic lymphocytic leukemia (CLL) blood or bone marrow express an antigen called CD38. CD38 levels are also predictive of CLL outcome. Other B-cell disorders, such as hairy cell leukemia and T-cell disorders, can also be characterized by flow cytometry, and MRD can also be pinpointed by the method.

Flow Cytometry For Solid Tumor Analysis

Currently, using flow cytometry to analyze solid tumors is not standard practice in most institutions. However, recent research has been directed toward expanding the possibilities of flow cytometry. In the event that it is applied, the method can be utilized to look for DNA content in either of two methods.

The number of chromosome sets present, or the ploidy, can affect the peak distribution on cytometry. Flow cytometry can be used to quantify the percentage of cells in the S phase of DNA synthesis. Then, that population can be examined. Even so, the interpretation of cytometric data for solid tumors has yet to be as well defined as for lymphoid malignancies.

Molecular Diagnostics In Cancer Diagnosis

Various molecular diagnostic techniques are utilized to scrutinize the nucleic acid content or protein gene products in samples from cancer patients. Many cancers are linked to specific gene mutations or their potential development. The initial step in all these techniques is the extraction of nucleic acids by cell disruption. A fresh blood sample is preferable, especially if RNA or DNA content is to be assessed. This decreases the risk of DNA degradation. The anti-coagulants of choice are either ethylenediaminetetraacetic acid (EDTor citrate since heparin can attach to nucleic acids. Some studies further suggest EDTA to be superior to citrate for plasma DNA testing. Proper storage conditions are critical if fresh samples cannot be promptly analyzed. Refrigeration for a few days is generally acceptable, and frozen, liquid nitrogen-stored, or paraffin-embedded older samples can sometimes be used.

Molecular Diagnostic Techniques

The two most commonly used types of molecular diagnostic techniques are polymerase chain reaction (PCR) and Southern blotting:

PCR amplifies the amount of DNA, which is usually used in other methodologies, such as sequencing. Reverse transcriptase enzyme generates DNA copies called cDNA from an RNA template with short nucleotide chains or oligonucleotides as primers. The number of cDNA copies is then usually amplified through a process called nesting.

Southern blotting typically uses enzymatic digestion of a patient sample, electrophoretic separation of the products, and then probing or blotting with suitable molecular probes. The latter methodology is labor-intensive and slow.

There are also relatively new techniques using microarrays involving gene chips that arrange up to a million different cDNA or nucleotide probes in a pattern onto glass. Because this involves such a high number of probes, This technique allows for the quantification of certain DNA sequences within the entire sample.

Aberrations Identified For Hematolymphoid-Derived Malignancies

Molecular diagnostic techniques are sometimes employed as adjuncts to other tests for hematolymphoid-derived neoplasms. The typical gene rearrangements observed for B-cell or T-cell malignancies are in the IgH or TCR genes, respectively. These rearrangements can be identified by Southern blotting or PCR. PCR is a particularly useful technique for pinpointing chromosomal translocations in tumor cells because of its sensitivity.

Thus, PCR is often employed when looking for minimal residual disease. Molecular diagnostic methods are typically used before bone marrow transplantation and utilize repetitive nucleotide sequences called simple tandem repeats or STRS to evaluate the likelihood of bone marrow transplantation success. The histocompatibility locus on chromosome 6 is targeted. In addition, these methods can also detect any viral DNA that has been integrated into the nuclear material of malignant cells.

Diagnosing Solid Tumors

A proportion of individuals with certain gene mutations are predisposed to hereditary cancer syndromes. Etiologically, only a few of these syndromes are localized in small genetic regions. Others are clearly more complex. Therefore, molecular diagnostic techniques are generally employed initially as screening assays for point mutations. PCR amplification is used in conjunction with either single-strand conformation polymorphism (SSCP) analysis or denaturing high-pressure liquid chromatography (DHPLC). PCR using larger probes, such as STRs, can be used to look for loss of heterozygosity (generally a deletion in the allele) in tumor cells relative to adjoining normal cells.

Techniques In Use Or In Development

Many tumor-specific markers have been identified, and more continue to be found. Knowledge of the presence of these markers in the blood or lymph can indicate metastases and aid in the determination of a patient's prognosis. Therefore, rapid PCR methods to detect these markers are in development.

There are many other ways to find proteins that are made by different genes and may be linked to cancer. Two-dimensional gels and laser techniques that excite the proteins are two examples. In the future, there will be tests for DNA methylation products and microarray tests that can find many of these expression products.

Tumor Marker Assays

Tumor marker assays measure the amount of certain molecules in serum, other body fluids, cells, and tissues that have been linked to cancer. Most of the available tests are either radioimmunoassays (RIAS) or enzyme-linked immunosorbent assays (ELISAs), which use radioisotopes or enzymes linked to different substances (often specific antibodies) as detection vehicles. The value of these immunoassays depends on how well they can tell the difference between normal tissue and cancerous or benign growths and how sensitive they are (the capacity for early detection during screening or preliminary diagnosis). The linearity of a test is also important because the changes in concentration must be able to be measured and must be directly linked to changes in the size of a tumor or how it responds to treatment. At the moment, measuring cancer or tumor markers is more useful for keeping an eye on a disease than for diagnosing it right away.

Tumor Markers Currently Used

For a tumor marker to be a good choice for a screening test, it should be specific to both the organ and the cancer. Some markers, like carcinoembryonic antigen (CEA), show that a malignant process is going on, but they are not specific to one organ. Total PSA, on the other hand, is the best cancer marker for early detection or screening because it is only found in the prostate.

There is a range of 4-10 ng/mL where noncancerous conditions like benign prostatic disease, or BPH, can also be picked up. When total PSA is added to free PSA, which is lower in men with prostate cancer, it makes it much easier to find prostate cancer.

In the same way, a carbohydrate marker called CA125 is a good way to check for ovarian cancer when used with other tests like ultrasound. So, PSA and CA125 are useful for screening, especially if they both go up when they are tested one after the other. These tests for screening are always done with serum or plasma.

Diagnostic And Prognostic Utility of Assays for Tumor Markers

Tumour markers have been found to be predictive of a tumor's response to treatment and prognosis, which has led researchers to believe that they may also be helpful in screening tests intended to find cancer early, before symptoms appear. Many of these markers are good adjuncts to tumor staging. Some of the more useful markers and their associated cancers follow:

- CA125: Useful for ovarian cancer diagnosis and monitoring in conjunction with other testing
- Alpha-fetoprotein or AFP: Informative for distinguishing between various types of germ cell tumors, especially when used together with a measurement of B-Human chorionic gonadotrophin (B-hCG)
- Carcinoembryonic antigen (CEA): Can be elevated in colorectal, breast, and lung carcinomas; however, elevated levels are not tumor-specific but can still be of prognostic or monitoring value
- Tissue estrogen and progesterone receptors: Have predictive utility for the treatment of breast cancer, as test-positive individuals are responsive to antiestrogen therapies
- Tissue HER-2/neu: Useful in the assessment of breast cancer patients for possible treatment with Herceptin.

Tumor Markers Useful for Monitoring Specific Malignancies

The following serum-based tumor marker assays are useful for monitoring the progression or remission of specific types of malignancies:

- Prostate cancer: PSA and prostate acid phosphatase
- Breast cancer: CA15-3, CA27.29, and for patients taking Herceptin, HER-2/neu

- Ovarian cancer: CA125
- Pancreatic cancer: CA19-9
- Colorectal cancer: CEA (also some limited utility for monitoring breast and lung cancers)
- Nonseminomatous testicular cancer: AFP
- Thyroid cancer: Thyroglobulin (contraindicated if the individual has autoantibodies)

Specific values are dependent on the immunoassay performed, so sequential values must be taken using the same test.

Monitoring Disease and Effectiveness of Treatment

The primary utility of most tumor marker assays is for the monitoring of disease progression and treatment effectiveness. After surgery, radiation, or other therapies, levels of certain markers should decrease within a few days if the treatment has significantly reduced the tumor burden. The lag time is dependent upon the half-life of the antigen in the serum and, sometimes, other factors such as renal clearance.

If levels increase after treatment, then the therapy has not worked, and sequential measurements that are increasing indicate possible disease progression. International recommendations for monitoring intervals suggest samples be taken quarterly. If levels increase linearly, the time between samples should be lowered to every 2-4 weeks.

Noninvasive Medical Imaging Tests

In general, a diagnostic or screening test is described by its sensitivity, specificity, and predictive value. Being sensitive means being able to notice small differences. It is measured by the number of real cases of disease for which a test is positive (when also accounting for false negatives). Specificity is the number of true negatives that the test does not mistake for false positives. The positive predictive value is a way to find out how many real cases of the disease the test finds.

These ideas can be used in different ways when it comes to imaging techniques. Positive tests can be looked at in one patient at a time to see how well they work as a screening test. You can also test the sensitivity, specificity, and predictive value of a single patient since they usually have more than one lesion or area with cancer cells. However, the accuracy of imaging tests depends a lot on the size of the lesion (very small ones might not be found) and the skill of the radiologist or other specialist who interprets the image.

Navigation and Coordination of Care

Patients diagnosed with cancer today have a difficult time figuring out how to receive treatment and making sense of the complex health care system. These issues begin as soon as a person receives a diagnosis and continue throughout treatment, follow-up care, and the experience of being a survivor. Patients who have cancer should put a significant amount of effort into comprehending their diagnoses and treatment options. However, due to the fragmented nature of our system and the numerous therapeutic options that can be pursued through screening, diagnosis, and therapy, a significant number of patients either put off beginning treatment for an excessive amount of time or do not receive treatment at all.

From the time that testing is completed until the beginning of therapy can range anywhere from sixty to one hundred and twenty days, according to the Centers for Disease Control and Prevention (CDC). Improvements in the treatment of cancer have managed to save the lives of millions of people over the past three decades (Jones, 2020). However, compared to the past, patients now have a significantly wider variety of options available to them for both their therapy and their aftercare.

Patients who have cancer need more diverse types of care, and it is taking them longer to acquire them during the preventive, screening, detection, and treatment stages of the disease.

And because a greater proportion of cancer patients have illnesses that last for a longer period of time, they make longer-term use of the health care system. Although hospitals have made efforts to simplify the system and facilitate improved collaboration among physicians, these efforts have yet to consistently keep pace with the rapid pace at which the system has evolved.

Utilizing patient advice is one approach that can be taken in order to resolve this issue. Evidence suggests that providing patients with guidance helps speed up cancer treatment, particularly in settings where patients' follow-up sessions are typically delayed the most.

Patient navigation programs were created to close care gaps by making it easier for people with cancer to get the services they need, to make sure those services were provided on time, and to give patients more help and direction. Cancer patients often face numerous challenges in accessing quality care, including scheduling appointments, coordinating transportation, and understanding complex treatment plans. Programs were developed to address these issues by providing individualized support and guidance to patients throughout their cancer journey.

These programs typically involve a trained navigator who acts as a point of contact for the patient, helping them navigate the health care system, connecting them with appropriate resources, and offering emotional support. By providing a more comprehensive approach to patient care, navigation programs can help improve patient outcomes and increase overall satisfaction with the healthcare experience.

Collaboration is needed not only with the patient but also with providers, families, and caregivers. This support is given at all stages of the cancer continuum, from preventing cancer and getting screened to post-treatment, survivorship, palliative, and end-of-life care.

As an introduction to the field of patient navigation, this section talks about what it does and how it helps provide high-quality oncology care.

Oncology Nurse Role

Oncology nurses work in acute care hospitals, ambulatory care clinics, private oncologists' offices, radiation therapy facilities, home health care agencies, and community agencies. Surgical, radiation, gynecologic, pediatric, and medical oncologists work with them. The Oncology Nursing Society (ONS) represents over 100,000 nurses and hosts more than 35,000 members as their professional association. The majority of ONS members are generalists who treat patients. Outpatient and home care occupations have increased as more patients receive care outside of hospitals. Cancer nurses do many tasks. Some focus on intensive bone marrow transplant care, while others screen, find, and stop cancer in the community.

Oncology nurses will alter as health care delivery changes and new scientific discoveries are applied in cancer care. Today's oncology nurses work in many fields that didn't exist ten years ago but are becoming more prominent. In ambulatory nurse-run centers, oncology nurses provide long-term follow-up, screenings before chemotherapy, fatigue management, and symptom management. As cancer genetics research has evolved, so has advanced practice nurses' involvement in counseling patients and assessing their risks. Oncology nurses can be CEOs, cancer service line directors, and hospital and clinic admissions heads.

The oncology nurse evaluates, teaches, coordinates, directs, manages symptoms, and supports patients. Oncology nurses provide direct patient care, manage symptoms, and provide supportive care, demonstrating their versatility and importance in cancer care.

Patient Assessment

Nurses must know a patient's mental and physical health, health behaviors, and how much the patient and family know about the disease and treatment. The oncology nurse discusses the treatment plan with the physician and knows the expected results and side effects. The nurse assesses the patient's mental and physical health. A comprehensive nursing history and physical are needed. Oncology nurses should understand all lab, pathology, and imaging results and their implications. Assessing the patient's knowledge about the condition and therapy is crucial to soothing them and creating a care plan. Knowing this will prevent misinterpretation and undue expectations. A well-prepared patient is more likely to adhere to treatment regimens, potentially improving treatment outcomes.

Exam findings inform a nursing care plan. At the minimum, this plan promotes:

(1) how well the patient understands therapy goals, plans, and side effects;
(2) psychologically and physically preparing for therapy;

(3) physical and mental ease;

(4) Compliance.

Patient Education

Most healthcare team members have less chance than the nurse to get to know patients and their families well enough to teach them. Patients and families are educated before, during, and after therapy. Treatment works better with constant encouragement. You can utilize written and visual instructional aids and refer people to specialists or community organizations like cancer support groups. This instruction helps individuals manage their diagnoses, long-term changes, and symptoms through planned and unplanned activities.

An example is that Lenalidomide is only available under the REVAssist® program to ensure patients are properly informed of fetal risks.

They learn how to prevent illness, be diagnosed, and seek treatment. Finally, individuals acquire the skills, knowledge, and attitudes needed to improve or maintain health. This customized education includes methods that suit the patient's goals, talents, and learning style. The ONS adds the following patient education outcome criteria. The patient and/or family should be able to:

1. describe the disease and therapy at a level appropriate to the patient's educational and emotional level,
2. participate in making decisions about the patient's care plan and daily activities, and
3. find the right community resources that offer information and services.

Efficient patient and family education is even more crucial as therapy is now provided outside hospitals. Nurses must know the adverse effects of each anticancer treatment and how to reduce its severity through self care. Discussion of routine issues and side effects is more effective than drug-specific discussions. Patients worry more about side effects and treatment than medicine efficacy.

Reviewing crucial points can help you attain the goal. Finding a pattern in the side effect sequence can calm patients and assist nurses in deciding what to do.

This may assist in distinguishing chemotherapy side effects from other illnesses with similar symptoms. Teaching patients about quick, early, delayed, and late side effects is easy.

Teaching tools and strategies vary on each patient's needs and ability. Discussion, reinforcement, and written, visual, and audiovisual educational resources are used. As the Internet improves, more cancer patients and their families use it to learn about the condition. Chat groups provide expertise and assistance. This conversational method of learning will increase.

In a personal notebook, patients should record daily questions, symptoms, prescription dates, and test dates. If the patient's medical record is unavailable, a personal journal provides written verification of when events and therapy began.

Coordination of Care

The oncology nurse ensures that all the complex cancer diagnosis and treatment instruments operate together. This coordination includes direct patient care, medical record-keeping, therapy, symptom management, connecting to other healthcare professionals, educating the patient and family, and counseling throughout diagnosis, therapy, and follow-up.

The patient should initially chat with the nurse. The patient and family should be able to call the cancer nurse during treatment. Stressing the need for phone communication is crucial since many patients travel far. Patients may always communicate with their doctors, obtain emergency help, and get daily emotional support.

Camp-Sorrell said most patient difficulties may be resolved without an office or emergency department visit. But, the nurse must learn enough to decide how to treat the patient. Many companies have guidelines for handling calls and other issues. These guidelines might help you diagnose a patient over the phone before calling the doctor and providing them with precise instructions for further treatment.

By using a diverse team, a cost-conscious staff speeds up modern cancer care in many regions. Talking amongst workers at different sites might take a lot of work. Patients who are terrified or bewildered benefit from the oncology nurse's communication and coordination abilities.

Direct Patient Care

Implanted ports have a lower risk of infection than tunneled central venous catheters.

The risk of secondary leukemia increases with the use of alkylating agents.

Most ONS members see and treat patients. Chemotherapy is approved nationally. Every school should have established guidelines for certifying chemotherapy, giving antineoplastic medications (all methods), handling and disposing of drugs safely, handling allergic reactions, and keeping records. The ONS course is for chemotherapeutic workers. These trainers can educate oncology nurses on community chemotherapy using ONS guidelines and a course.

Patients receiving chemotherapy must receive the proper dose and medicine in the right manner, which is a crucial task for nurses. In a survey of ONS members about medication errors, 63% stated they saw evidence of them in patient care settings (Chaudhury, Mahmood, & Valente, 2006) Misdosing, administration, and manufacturing of medications were among these blunders.

The Institute of Medicine found that drug errors kill more people than workplace injuries. A nationwide effort aims to reduce medical errors and improve patient safety. This plan affects states and neighborhoods. The ONS's 2001 position statement on "Prevention and Reporting of Medication Errors" recommends safe treatment through practice, policy, systems, education, and study. Individual and institutional rules can reduce chemotherapeutic errors. These regulations should contain a means to report mistakes and a plan to evaluate current practices and make adjustments to prevent them.

Managing Symptoms

Oncology nurses deal with various indicators that cancer patients and their families experience due to disease or treatment every day. Nurses group patients' issues and help doctors diagnose and treat them. The nurse uses subjective and objective data like the patient's history and last chemotherapy treatment to treat and care for them. Chemotherapy's side effects have improved, thanks to nurses. For instance, nausea and vomiting are common chemotherapy side effects. Nursing research prioritizes controlling these symptoms. Nausea and vomiting have been studied extensively, and instruments have been developed to track their frequency, pain, and emotional impact. This knowledge helps cure nausea and vomiting and evaluate prescription medications.

Massage therapy involves the manipulation of soft tissues through applying pressure, tension, or vibration to specific areas of the body. It is often used in oncology care to provide pain relief, reduce anxiety, and improve overall well-being. Massage therapy helps to relax muscles, promote blood circulation, and release endorphins, which can help patients manage pain and alleviate symptoms associated with cancer treatment.

Hair loss from chemotherapy usually begins two weeks after beginning treatment.

Xerostomia, or dry mouth, is a common side effect of chemotherapy. Spicy and acidic foods can exacerbate the dryness and discomfort experienced by patients with xerostomia.

Palmar-plantar erythrodysesthesia changes to skin can be related to capillary rupture occurring while walking or during other weight-bearing activities.

Induced bone marrow suppression can cause a decrease in red blood cells, leading to anemia. This delayed-onset side effect usually occurs several months after radiation therapy completion.

Chemotherapy drugs often affect the bone marrow, leading to a reduction in platelets (thrombocytopenia). Platelets play a crucial role in blood clotting, and a low platelet count can put patients at risk for bleeding and bruising. Monitoring platelet count throughout the treatment helps in predicting and preventing potential complications, such as hemorrhage or delayed wound healing. Oncology certified nurses should educate patients about signs of abnormal bleeding and promptly report any significant decline in platelet count, ensuring appropriate intervention to maintain patient safety.

Skin redness, fatigue, and an increased risk of infection are potential side effects of radiation therapy, and they should be addressed in the patient's education.

Radiation therapy can suppress the bone marrow, causing a decrease in the production of neutrophils, leading to neutropenia. This leaves patients susceptible to infections.

By being aware of their bowel habits, a patient will be able to better plan sexual activities around expected bowel movements when they have a permanent colostomy.

Chemotherapy, especially with cisplatin and alkylating agents can cause permanent infertility (azoospermia). Sperm banking is recommended prior to the start of treatment if the patient is interested in future paternity.

 It is recommended that the patient avoid inserting anything into the vagina for four weeks following a loop electrosurgical excision procedure.

Lymphedema rates are 0% to 5% for women after a sentinel lymph node procedure and 10%-30% after axillary lymph node dissection.

Pneumonitis is an inflammatory condition of the lung parenchyma that can occur as a complication of immunotherapy. Symptoms include dyspnea, cough, chest pain, and decreased breath sounds on physical examination, along with the presence of a pleural effusion. It is important to recognize and manage pneumonitis promptly as it can lead to respiratory failure if left untreated.

Chemotherapy treatment providers must evaluate their medical and nursing expenditures due to reduced funding and rising healthcare prices. Oncology nurses contributed antiemetic guidelines, notably for 5-hydroxytryptamine receptor blockers. These guidelines for safe and effective antiemetic medication administration have been proven to reduce costs.

Cancer patients believe fatigue is the worst side effect of treatment, which nurses have helped them manage. Nurse specialists have improved fatigue definition, frequency, measurement, and treatment. In many respects, the ONS has helped manage cancer fatigue.

Changes in appetite and weight loss are commonly observed in individuals suffering from depression. Fatigue, insomnia, and feelings of guilt are all common signs of depression. Understanding the typical symptoms of depression is crucial for an Oncology Certified Nurse as it helps in recognizing and addressing potential psychosocial distress that patients may experience during their cancer journey.

Chronic lung cancer-associated symptoms primarily develop due to long-term exposure to cigarette smoke, leading to chronic inflammation in the lungs. This inflammation can trigger persistent cough, dyspnea (shortness of breath), wheezing, and in advanced cases, clubbing of fingers.

Epidemiology

A thorough understanding of cancer epidemiology is crucial for obtaining information about the population trends and potential causes of these illnesses. This information enables the establishment of prompt and suitable health care interventions with the goal of creating effective prevention, screening, and diagnosis policies.

Cancer epidemiology involves many statistical quantities. Below is a list of some of the quantities important to cancer epidemiology. Most of these quantities are stated either as a percentage or as a number of cases per 100,000 individuals. Most of these statistics can be found not only as aggregated (all cancers) statistics but also broken out by type of cancer, gender, ethnicity, and other characteristics.

Incidence rate refers to the number of new cases that are diagnosed in a given period, typically a year. It is reported as the number of cases per 100,000 individuals.

The attack rate is a measure used to calculate the incidence rate of a disease in a population during an outbreak or an epidemic. It is calculated by dividing the number of new cases of the disease by the total population at risk during a specified time period. The attack rate helps determine the risk of acquiring the disease in the population and is particularly useful in infectious disease epidemiology.

Prevalence rate refers to the total number of cases that were active during any part of a given period, typically a year. It is reported as the number of cases per 100,000 individuals. Prevalence rates are always higher than incidence rates for the same time period since prevalence rates count all the same cases that incidence rates do, plus all previously diagnosed cases that are still active.

Mortality rate (or death rate) refers to the number of people who died from a particular disease during a given time period, typically a year. It is reported as the number of deaths per 100,000 individuals.

Case-fatality rate (CFR) refers to the mortality rate among only those diagnosed with a particular disease. It is reported as a percentage. CFR is a useful metric for evaluating how deadly a particular type of cancer is or comparing it among different types of cancer.

Survival rate refers to the likelihood of living at least a given length of time, usually 5 or 10 years, after having been diagnosed with a particular disease. It is reported as a percentage. Absolute risk refers to the likelihood of being diagnosed with a particular disease in a given time period. This time period can be stated as a set length of time (e.g., within five years), prior to a given age (e.g., before the age of 40), or at any point in an individual's entire lifetime. It can be expressed as a percentage or as numerical odds (e.g., 12 out of 100,000). Percentages are typically preferred when the value is at least 0.1%.

Relative risk refers to the likelihood of being diagnosed with a particular disease among those subject to an identified risk factor for the disease. Risk factors may be intrinsic (e.g., age, gender, ethnicity, BMI, other diseases present), behavioral (e.g., smoking, drinking alcohol, sedentary lifestyle), or environmental (e.g., air quality, substance exposure). Relative risk is expressed in the same terms as absolute risk.

Attributable risk refers to the difference in likelihood of being diagnosed with a particular disease between those exposed to a risk factor and those not exposed.

It essentially expresses how much of a person's risk for a disease is due to a particular risk factor (e.g., how much more likely is someone to develop lung cancer given that they smoke?).

Survivorship

While several programmes have adopted survivorship care in different ways, most programs are managed by advanced practise clinicians, such as nurse practitioners, or physicians. Every program strategy has benefits and drawbacks of its own. For instance, while some survivorship care programs stress wellness and the value of psychological support, others concentrate on addressing the consequences of cancer and provide care for long-term and late side effects of treatment.

The patient population and the quantity and kind of resources available in the practise environment are the two primary factors to take into account while creating a survivorship care program. Patients with cancer may face a range of demands and experiences over the course of their disease, from minor side effects to chronic illnesses or serious health problems brought on by therapy.

Supportive Care

Oncology nurses assist cancer patients and their families with several supportive care issues. Among them, pain management and survivor support stand out.

Loss of personal control can lead to feelings of frustration and anger in patients. By involving the patient in determining the timing of activities and care, the nurse empowers them to maintain a sense of autonomy. This intervention promotes patient-centered care, fosters a sense of empowerment, and supports the patient's emotional well-being. It is crucial to facilitate opportunities for patients to actively participate in decision- making related to their care to enhance their sense of control and improve overall satisfaction.

Nursing care should help patients feel better, educate them and their families on pain management, discuss and assist with behavioral and physical interventions, reduce drug side effects, and encourage patients to keep their treatment and follow-up appointments. The nurse should explain treatments and let patients and families ask questions. The patient should be informed of medicine names, dosages, side effects, and antiemetics. Constipation remedies should be discussed, too. The nurse should monitor the patient's mental and cognitive capacities, breathing, and bowel motions, as well as medicine efficacy. Patients and their families should know how to contact medical staff in an emergency and feel comfortable doing so.

Advance Care Planning

Advance care planning, or ACP, lets people choose ahead of time how they want to be treated medically at the end of their lives. Advance directives (ADs) are meant to give patients more control over their own healthcare decisions, help families and healthcare workers make decisions when a patient isn't able to, match personal values with end-of-life choices, and make it more likely that patients' wishes will be carried out.

The American Cancer Society (NCS) (2011) says that ACP includes clear conversations about the patient's prognosis, information about ADs, an explanation of the do-not-resuscitate (DNR) choice, information about palliative care options (such as hospice), and talks about where the patient would like to die.

A healthcare proxy, a living will, or a "Five Wishes document" are all legal forms that patients can use to say how they want their medical decisions to be made or who they would like to make those decisions if they become too sick or injured to do so themselves. A DNR order says that resuscitation should not be tried on someone who has heart or respiratory arrest, and it can be given because of an AD.

The goals of ADs are to list the patient's preferences for end-of-life care, which helps healthcare workers understand what the patient wants, improves the quality of death, and lessens the stress on family and caregivers. The Patient Self-Determination Act of 1990 says that healthcare facilities that get Medicare and Medicaid funds must tell patients about their right to make choices about their care and put written information on ADs.

Challenges of Incorporating ACP in Oncology Care

Advance care planning (ACP) is a crucial process for patients with advanced cancer to articulate their values, preferences, and goals to make decisions for their future care. Providing high-quality palliative care ensures patients' dignity, closure, and meaningful time with loved ones.

A care plan should be made for every person who is known to be dying. To be good at ACP, you need to have a lot of training, practice, and fine-tuning of your skills and sensitivity. The current strategic focus on ACP is good, but it should turn into something other than a checklist activity in a society that is focused on goals.

Hospital doctors need to be able to spot patients who are in their last year of life and start a conversation with their primary care team. ACP is a voluntary process that moves at the patient's pace, so both primary and secondary care may need to help with it. It is important to create ways for patients, caregivers, and healthcare teams to work together, and ACP training should be made available.

Though at varying rates across the globe, the survivor cadre is expanding. Cancer survivorship nurses are in a unique position to help patients who have received cancer treatment get ready for and make a smooth transition to this next stage of their journey.

Opportunities to learn more about the survival experience and its impact on the long-term quality of life of cancer survivors would be beneficial for nurses who wish to support cancer survivors. In order to support their practice in providing long-term monitoring and health maintenance along the continuum of cancer care with survivors, nurses would also be well-served by learning more about the best available evidence.

The End-of-Life Care Strategy (DH 2008) acknowledges the inequity in quality and choice in end-of-life care and outlines an ambitious agenda to address this. ACP is a key element, aiming to fulfill patient goals such as participation in treatment decisions, preparation for death, achieving a sense of completion, and being in familiar surroundings with family and friends.

Chapter Three: Oncology Nursing Practice

Since the number of cancer patients is going up, there needs to be a steady supply of good oncology nurses. When you know more about the background of oncology nursing, you can make practice settings that will draw and keep specialized oncology nurses.

Understanding Staging and Grading of Cancer

Staging is a process that assesses the size of the tumor, degree of local invasion, and presence of metastases to determine the extent and spread of cancer in the body. It helps in planning appropriate treatment strategies and predicting prognosis. On the other hand, histological grading involves evaluating the appearance and differentiation of cancer cells under a microscope.

It classifies cancer cells into different grades based on their resemblance to normal cells and determines the aggressiveness of the tumor. This information is crucial in guiding treatment decisions and predicting the likelihood of cancer progression.

Patient Self-Exams

Self-breast exams should be performed 7 to 10 days after the start of menses (the patient's period...this is the first day of bleeding). Breast tissue is soft at this time due to hormone levels.

The best time to perform a self-testicular exam is after a shower when the scrotum is descended and the tissue is soft. This makes it easier to feel lumps or masses.

Medical Staff Safety

Sealed radiation therapy patients are radioactive for 4-8 hours. Staff should be rotated out and never required to provide care for more than one patient at a time. This decreases radiation exposure.

Blood Counts

Patients who have undergone a bone marrow transplant are at major risk for bleeding and infection. The bone marrow is responsible for producing infection and bleeding-fighting agents such as WBCs and platelets. Therefore, when a patient receives this from a donor, it takes time for the body to build up normal levels.

A patient with leukemia is entering the period known as "the nadir". As the nurse, you know the patient is at greatest risk for bleeding, and the patient can experience a platelet count of 50,000 or less. During this period, bone marrow suppression is the greatest; therefore, the platelet count may be extremely low.

Clinically, a patient with leukemia will present with decreased hgb and hct, decreased platelets, and elevated or normal WBCs with enlarged lymph nodes. This is because leukemia affects the bone marrow. The bone marrow is a vital organ that is responsible for producing platelets, white blood cells, and red blood cells.

Multiple myeloma is proliferation of plasma cells. This causes increased uric acid and calcium levels. This, therefore, increases the patient's risk for renal failure and bone problems. Encourage fluids to keep the kidneys "flushed" and skeletal support for the bones helps with further complications.

Patient Care

The priority intervention for a patient with advanced lung cancer experiencing dyspnea and tachypnea is administering supplemental oxygen. This intervention helps increase the oxygen level in the blood, relieving the respiratory distress. Deep breathing exercises help improve lung expansion, but they might be challenging for patients with advanced lung cancer. Administering corticosteroids may be appropriate for some patients, but it is not the priority intervention in managing dyspnea and tachypnea. Encouraging frequent rest periods may provide some relief, but it is not as effective as administering supplemental oxygen in addressing the underlying issue.

Dyspnea in patients with advanced lung cancer can be relieved by nonpharmacological approaches, and relaxation techniques like guided imagery and deep breathing exercises can help decrease anxiety and dyspnea.

When a patient develops radiation-induced dermatitis, it is important to prioritize interventions that promote skin integrity and minimize further damage. Applying corticosteroid creams may be beneficial in some cases, but the nurse should prioritize gentle skin care first. The use of hot water and tight-fitting clothing can further irritate the skin and should be avoided. Using mild soap and patting the skin dry gently helps maintain cleanliness without causing excessive friction or trauma to the affected area.

When administering immunotherapy, the sudden onset of rash, difficulty breathing, and swelling around the face and lips suggests a severe allergic reaction, such as anaphylaxis. The priority action for the nurse would be to assess Sarah's vital signs and respiratory status to determine the severity of the reaction and initiate appropriate interventions. Administering an antihistamine may be necessary, but it is not the first action in managing anaphylaxis. Continuing the immunotherapy treatment would not be appropriate if Sarah is experiencing an allergic reaction. Documenting the reaction is important but not the immediate priority in this situation.

When faced with a patient's family suggesting complementary and alternative medicine (CAM), such as ginger and acupuncture interventions to alleviate symptoms or side effects, it is essential for the oncology nurse to approach the situation with evidence-based practice principles. The nurse should conduct a literature review to gather evidence on the effectiveness of ginger and acupuncture in managing chemotherapy-induced nausea and vomiting. By critically appraising the current research, the nurse can provide the family with an informed opinion and guide them towards evidence-based CAM interventions, if appropriate. This approach allows the nurse to uphold the standards of practice while considering the patient's preferences and optimizing symptom management.

The presence of bilateral lower-extremity weakness and changes in bowel and bladder function indicate significant spinal cord compression. The most appropriate intervention in this scenario is to initiate immediate radiation therapy to relieve the compression and prevent further neurological damage. Opioid analgesics can be given for pain relief, but the priority should be addressing the spinal cord compression. Ambulation may worsen the condition, and ice packs are not effective in relieving spinal cord compression. Prompt intervention is crucial to preserve neurological function in patients with spinal cord compression.

Blood and marrow transplant can be performed using the patient's own healthy cells through an autologous transplant or cells from a donor through an allogeneic transplant. Autologous transplant is commonly used in the treatment of non-malignant diseases, such as aplastic anemia, while allogeneic transplant is often utilized in the treatment of hematological malignancies like leukemia. The choice between autologous and allogeneic transplant depends on the patient's specific condition and individual factors, such as age, overall health, and availability of a suitable donor.

When a patient has impaired mobility due to musculoskeletal alterations, it is important to promote joint flexibility and prevent further decline in functioning. Assisting the patient with range of motion exercises helps maintain joint mobility, prevent contractures, and preserve muscle strength. Encouraging bed rest may lead to further muscle atrophy and decreased range of motion. Administering muscle relaxants and providing heat therapy can offer temporary relief but do not directly address the issue of impaired mobility.

When a patient complains of severe abdominal pain, nausea, and vomiting and physical examination reveals abdominal distention with decreased bowel sounds and the patient has not passed stool for the past 48 hours, this is an indication of bowel obstruction. Surgical intervention is necessary to relieve the obstruction and restore bowel function. Prompt surgical management not only reduces the risk of bowel perforation but also provides symptomatic relief to the patient, thereby improving her overall condition and quality of life.

Patient Support

As an oncology nurse, it is important to address the psychosocial dimensions of care, including financial concerns. Providing information on community resources for financial assistance can help alleviate the financial burden experienced by oncology patients. These resources may include charities, non-profit organizations, and government programs that offer financial aid, grants, or assistance with medical bills and other expenses. By equipping patients with knowledge about available resources, nurses can support them in accessing the financial help they may need during their cancer journey.

Discrimination concerns in survivorship care refer to the challenges faced by cancer survivors due to their diagnosis. This can include instances where individuals are treated unfairly or experience negative behaviors because they have had cancer. It is important for oncology nurses to address these concerns and provide support to patients who may be facing discrimination. By recognizing and addressing the prejudicial treatment or negative experiences faced by cancer survivors, healthcare professionals can foster a more inclusive and supportive care environment for their patients.

Negative interactions within social relationships and dysfunctional family dynamics can lead to heightened emotional distress, such as increased rates of depression and anxiety. It is important for oncology nurses to identify and address these negative influences, as they can significantly impact a patient's overall well-being and quality of life. By recognizing the impact of social relationships and family dynamics, nurses can offer appropriate support and interventions to enhance psychosocial care for their patients.

Fentanyl is a potent opioid analgesic commonly used for the management of severe breakthrough cancer pain. It is available in various formulations including transdermal patches, oral lozenges, and nasal spray. Fentanyl acts on the central nervous system to provide rapid pain relief, making it an effective choice for acute episodes of pain that are not controlled by the patient's regular analgesic regimen. It is important for oncology certified nurses to be knowledgeable about the appropriate use of opioids such as fentanyl in the management of cancer-related pain to ensure optimal pain control and quality of life for their patients. Acetaminophen, gabapentin, and amitriptyline have analgesic properties but are not the first-line medications for breakthrough cancer pain.

Teaching deep breathing exercises and progressive muscle relaxation techniques can help patients with cancer manage their anxiety effectively. These techniques promote relaxation, reduce muscle tension, and decrease physiological symptoms associated with anxiety.

Emotional distress is a common aspect of survivorship and may result from the psychosocial impact of cancer diagnosis, treatment, and ongoing life adjustments. It is important to assess and address emotional distress to support patients' overall well-being during their survivorship journey. Nurses play a crucial role in providing emotional support, connecting patients to appropriate resources, and helping them navigate through their emotional challenges.

Chemotherapy agents such as taxanes and platinum compounds are known to cause peripheral neuropathy by damaging the peripheral nerves. This can lead to sensory changes, such as numbness, tingling, and decreased sensation in the affected areas. It is important for oncology nurses to recognize and manage peripheral neuropathy to improve the quality of life for patients undergoing chemotherapy.

Physical therapy is a widely used rehabilitation intervention for cancer survivors to improve physical functioning and overall quality of life. It focuses on restoring mobility, reducing pain, and enhancing strength and flexibility through various exercises and techniques. Physical therapy helps to manage treatment-related side effects, such as decreased range of motion and muscle weakness, and it promotes independence and optimal functioning. While other options, such as yoga and meditation, cognitive-behavioral therapy, and art therapy, may have psychological and emotional benefits for cancer survivors, they are not primarily aimed at addressing physical functioning and quality of life.

Chemotherapy often results in gastrointestinal side effects such as nausea, vomiting, and loss of weight and malnutrition. Encouraging the patient to eat small, frequent meals that are easy to digest and are nutrient-dense can help manage their symptoms while providing nutrients to support their nutritional status. This approach allows the patient to maintain their caloric intake despite their reduced appetite and can minimize the gastrointestinal distress caused by heavy meals.

Chapter Four: Treatment Modalities

When it comes to treating cancer, there are several options available. The main objectives of these treatments are to control the spread of the disease, eliminate it and prevent it from coming back. The most effective treatment is one that is tailored to the patient's profile and takes into account various factors, such as their overall health and medical history, the type of tumor, as well as its location and distribution.

The doctor decides the treatment plan based on all these factors. Treatment modalities vary from patient to patient and can include surgery, radiation therapy, chemotherapy, and targeted therapy. Targeted therapy can further include gene expression modulators, immunotherapy, angiogenesis inhibitors, and hormone therapy, among others.

Surgical and Procedural Interventions

Surgical and procedural interventions play a crucial role in oncology care. They involve various surgical techniques and procedures aimed at diagnosing, treating, and managing cancer. One of the most common surgical interventions is a biopsy, which involves removing a small sample of tissue for examination and diagnosis. This procedure is important as it helps determine the type and stage of cancer, guiding further treatment decisions. Another common intervention is the removal of tumors through surgery, also known as tumor resection. This can be done through open surgery or minimally invasive techniques such as laparoscopy or robotic-assisted surgery.

Surgical interventions can be curative in some cases, aiming to remove the cancerous tissues completely. This is often the case for localized tumors that have not spread to other parts of the body. Surgical resections can help eliminate tumors in organs such as the breast, colon, lung, or prostate. In cases where complete removal is not possible, surgery can still be used to debulk the tumor, reducing its size and relieving symptoms.

Surgical procedures can serve as an access point for various treatments. For example, the insertion of a port or catheter enables the direct administration of chemotherapy or other medications into the bloodstream. This helps to reduce the need for repeated needle insertions and provides patients with a more comfortable treatment experience. Additionally, surgical interventions can alleviate cancer-related symptoms and enhance the quality of life. These interventions may include the removal of tumor-caused blockages, such as relieving bowel or urinary obstructions. Palliative surgeries can also be performed to manage pain or improve mobility.

Graft-versus-host disease (GVHD) is a common complication associated with blood and marrow transplant (BMT). GVHD occurs when the transplanted donor cells recognize the recipient's tissues as foreign and attack them. This immune response can manifest as acute or chronic GVHD and can affect various organs, including the skin, gastrointestinal tract, and liver. It is important for nurses to closely monitor patients undergoing BMT for signs and symptoms of GVHD and provide appropriate interventions to manage and prevent complications.

For a bronchoscopy with biopsy, the patient should be NPO for at least 8 hours before the procedure to minimize the risk of aspiration during sedation. NPO status ensures an empty stomach, reducing the likelihood of regurgitation or vomiting while the patient is under conscious sedation. It is essential for the nurse to provide clear instructions regarding fasting before the procedure to ensure patient safety and optimal conditions for the bronchoscopy.

Oncology nurses need to have a thorough understanding of surgical and procedural interventions. They have a vital role in preoperative and postoperative care, working closely with the surgical team to guarantee the safety of the patients and achieve optimal outcomes. Nurses provide education and support to patients and their families by explaining the purpose and expectations of surgical interventions, as well as potential complications and recovery processes.

Radiation Therapy

Radiation therapy is a frequently used treatment method in oncology for battling cancer. It involves using high-energy radiation beams to locate and destroy cancer cells. This therapy can be administered externally or internally, depending on the type and location of the tumor.

External radiation therapy, also known as external beam radiation, is the most common form of radiation therapy. It involves directing a focused beam of radiation from an external machine toward the tumor. This beam of radiation damages the DNA of cancer cells, preventing their ability to divide and grow. The treatment is typically painless and delivered on an outpatient basis over several weeks.

Internal radiation therapy, also known as brachytherapy, involves placing a radiation source directly into or near the tumor. This allows for a higher concentration of radiation to be delivered to the cancer cells while minimizing damage to surrounding healthy tissues. This method is often used for cancers in the cervix, prostate, and breast.

Radiation therapy can be used with the goal of cure, control, or palliation. In curative intent, the radiation is usually delivered with the intent of eradicating the tumor. In control intent, the goal is to shrink or slow down the growth of the tumor. Palliative radiation aims to relieve symptoms and improve the quality of life by reducing pain or pressure caused by the tumor.

To ensure the safety and effectiveness of radiation therapy, the oncology nurse plays a crucial role in educating patients about the treatment, managing side effects, and providing emotional support. The nurse also monitors the patient's progress and collaborates with the radiation oncologist and other healthcare providers to ensure comprehensive care. Radiation therapy is a common treatment modality used in oncology to fight cancer. It involves using high-energy radiation beams to target and destroy cancer cells. This therapy can be delivered externally or internally, depending on the type and location of the tumor.

Chemotherapy

Chemotherapy is a widely used treatment in the field of oncology. It involves administering drugs to kill or prevent the multiplication of cancer cells. This method is often recommended for patients with different types and stages of cancer and can be used as the primary treatment or in combination with other therapies.

The purpose of chemotherapy is to target cancer cells that might have spread throughout the whole body, not just in the primary tumor site. There are different ways to administer this treatment, including intravenously, orally, topically, or by injection into a specific body cavity. The choice of administration depends on factors such as the type and stage of cancer, the drugs being used, and the patient's overall health.

Chemotherapy drugs work by disrupting the cell division process of cancer cells, either killing the cells directly or slowing down their growth. Alkalyting agents break the DNA helix strand and interfere with DNA replication.

Side effects of chemotherapy are different depending on the drugs used and the individual patient. They include hair loss, nausea, fatigue, vomiting, and an increased risk of infection. Chemotherapy will decrease the response by the immune system by causing neutropenia, anemia, and thrombocytopenia, collectively known as Myelosuppression.

Patients receiving oxaliplatin should be instructed to avoid ice and cold foods and fluids during the infusion.

In a pregnant woman, chemotherapy started after the first trimester has fewer complications and poses less risk to the fetus than chemotherapy given during the first trimester.

Life-threatening adverse reactions to posaconazole can include Torsades de Pointes, hepatocellular damage, and allergic reactions.

Oncology nurses play a crucial role in managing these side effects and providing support to patients throughout their treatment.

The nurse should be familiar with the different methods of administering different drugs, and which methods are safe for which drug. Some of the administration methods are intramuscular, intraperitoneal, subcutaneous, and intrathecal. Vincristine is fatal if administered intrathecally, for example, so this is important.

Nursing care management of the patient receiving intraperitoneal drug administration includes encouraging repositioning from side to side every 15 minutes during the dwell time.

Before starting chemotherapy, patients undergo a thorough evaluation, including imaging studies, blood tests, and other diagnostic procedures. This helps determine the most appropriate drugs and dosage for each patient. Regular monitoring during treatment is essential to assess effectiveness, manage side effects, and adjust the treatment plan as needed. Chemotherapy is often given in cycles, with rest moments in between to allow the body to recover. Nadir varies but typically occurs 7-10 days after chemotherapy. The length and number of cycles depend on various factors, including the type and stage of cancer, the drugs used, and the response to treatment. In some cases, chemotherapy may be used before surgery or radiation therapy to shrink tumors, making them easier to remove or treat.

Targeted Therapy

Biotherapy, also known as targeted therapy, aims to specifically target and interfere with the growth and spread of cancer cells by targeting specific molecules involved in their development. It can be effective in both hematologic malignancies and solid tumors, including breast cancer. By using medications such as monoclonal antibodies, tyrosine kinase inhibitors, or immune checkpoint inhibitors, biotherapy offers a more targeted and precise approach to cancer treatment, reducing damage to healthy cells and potentially improving the patient's outcomes.

Allogeneic stem cell transplant types may be either myeloablative or nonmyeloablative and can be used to treat acute lymphocytic leukemia, among other malignant and nonmalignant blood disorders.

Hormone therapy has been successfully used to treat breast and prostate cancers.

Epidermal growth factor receptor inhibitors work inside the cell to block binding on the intracellular portion of the receptor.

Chimeric antibodies are made up of approximately 70% human and 30% foreign antibodies.

Monoclonal antibodies bind to the tumor cell and prevent ligand-receptor binding by blocking other molecules from attaching to the cell, thus preventing the rapid growth of cancer cells.

Immunotherapy such as the combination of anti-PD-1 and anti-CTLA-4 antibodies can lead to immune-related colitis as a side effect. Diarrhea is one of the common manifestations. It is essential to assess the severity of colitis and initiate appropriate management promptly to prevent complications such as bowel perforation or sepsis.

Patient Support

As an Oncology Certified Nurse, providing emotional support to patients and their families is an essential aspect of the nurse's scope of practice. This includes listening to patients' concerns, addressing their emotional needs, and offering guidance and resources to cope with the challenges of cancer.

Providing emotional support is a crucial aspect of the nursing process and reflects the standards of care for oncology nursing practice. Encouraging the patient to verbalize their fears and concerns about treatment, addresses the patient's emotional well-being. This allows for effective communication, support, and identification of any potential psychosocial factors that may impact the treatment..

It is essential to initially evaluate a patient's vital signs to rule out any physical causes of depression symptoms, such as anemia or hormonal imbalances, that may mimic depression symptoms. Depression assessment should include ruling out physical causes before considering psychological factors.

Deep breathing helps activate the body's relaxation response by slowing down the heart rate, promoting a sense of calm, and reducing anxiety symptoms.

If a patient says that certain things, such as reading medical information makes them anxious, look for an alternate system that doesn't produce so much anxiety. In this case, providing the patient with visual aids can enhance their understanding and reduce anxiety related to reading complex medical information.

Research has shown that visual learning is often preferred by oncology patients due to its ability to enhance comprehension and memory retention. Visual aids can help patients conceptualize complex medical concepts, understand treatment procedures, and retain information related to self-care and management of symptoms. They can help medical staff provide clear, concise, and easily understandable information to patients.

A patient exhibiting profound fatigue, anorexia, and generalized muscle weakness can be taught energy conservation techniques to help them preserve their energy, prioritize activities, and reduce unnecessary exertion. This intervention is crucial in helping patients maximize their independence and cope with limited physical capabilities.

Elevating the head of the bed helps to alleviate the symptoms of superior vena cava syndrome (SVCS) by reducing venous congestion and facilitating venous return. This position decreases the pressure exerted on the superior vena cava, thus reducing the severity of symptoms.

The recommended intervention for managing lymphedema in oncology patients is to apply tight bandages or compression garments to the affected limb. This helps to improve lymphatic flow, reduce swelling, and provide support.

Chapter Five: Symptom Management and Palliative Care

Palliative care is a type of medical care that is provided to people who have a serious or life-threatening illness, such as cancer. It is a type of care that is designed to improve the quality of life of patients and their families by offering relief from the symptoms, pain, and stress that arise from the illness. Palliative care is not constrained to patients who are nearing the end of life. It can be given to patients at any stage of their illness, and it can be administered alongside curative treatments.

It ensures the management of symptoms such as fatigue, pain, nausea, and shortness of breath. The care team works to prevent or treat these symptoms as early as possible so that the patient can maintain their quality of life. Additionally, palliative care addresses the emotional and social needs of the patient and their family. The care team provides counseling, support, and assistance with advance care planning and decision-making.

Patients can receive palliative care in various settings, such as hospitals, outpatient clinics, or their own homes. A team of healthcare professionals or a single healthcare provider can provide the care. Age or stage of illness are not criteria for the provision of palliative care.

Many of the same treatments that are used to treat cancer can also be used for palliative care. For instance, chemotherapy or radiation therapy can be utilized to manage the symptoms of the disease. Surgery may also be performed to alleviate pain and other symptoms. The care team works closely with the patient and their family to determine the best course of action that will help the patient maintain their quality of life.

Acute symptoms are those that appear suddenly and have a short duration. These symptoms can arise due to various causes, such as the administration of chemotherapy, radiation therapy, or surgical procedures. Common examples include nausea, vomiting, pain, and fatigue. Acute symptoms are often managed through pharmacological interventions and supportive care measures. It is essential for nurses to promptly assess and address acute symptoms to improve patient comfort and overall well-being.

Morphine is the gold standard for managing severe cancer pain due to its potency and effectiveness.

Transcutaneous electrical nerve stimulation (TENS) is a non-pharmacological intervention that helps in managing pain for cancer patients. It involves the use of a device that delivers low-voltage electrical currents to the skin, reducing pain by blocking pain signals. TENS is often used in conjunction with analgesics or as an alternative method of pain relief.

Acupuncture is a complementary modality that involves the insertion of thin needles into specific points on the body. It is based on traditional Chinese medicine principles and aims to restore the flow of energy, known as Qi, throughout the body. By stimulating these specific points, acupuncture can help alleviate symptoms such as pain, nausea, and fatigue, commonly experienced by cancer patients.

A different example of managing patient pain is in caring for patients with brain metastasis who complain of severe headaches, difficulty with coordination, and changes in their levels of consciousness. Elevating the head of the bed promotes venous drainage and helps reduce intracranial pressure. It is an essential intervention in managing increased intracranial pressure, which can help alleviate the symptoms and prevent further complications.

Who Gives Palliative Care?

Usually, healthcare professionals who have received extensive training and/or certification in palliative care provide it. These specialists offer comprehensive, holistic care to both the patient and their family or caregiver, addressing not only the physical symptoms of cancer but also the emotional, social, and spiritual issues that arise during this challenging experience. This includes addressing pain, shortness of breath, fatigue, nausea, depression, anxiety, and other symptoms that can significantly impact a patient's quality of life.

Fatigue is a common side effect of cancer treatment, and it is important for patients to conserve energy. Pushing oneself to do more can worsen fatigue and may lead to a decrease in overall energy levels. Rest and pacing activities are essential strategies to manage fatigue.

The specialists work in a team with various healthcare professionals, including doctors, nurses, therapists, and social workers. This team collaborates with the oncology care team to manage the patient's care and ensure the best possible quality of life. They assess the patient's needs and develop a personalized plan of care that may include medication management, counseling, physical therapy, nutrition support, and spiritual care. The Wong-Baker faces pain scale is an essential tool in assessing the patient's pain level.

In addition to caring for the patient, palliative care specialists provide support to caregivers, who often experience significant emotional and physical strain while caring for their loved one. They facilitate communication among team members, assist in discussions focusing on the patient's goals of care, and help ensure that the patient's wishes are honored. Overall, palliative care is an essential component of cancer care that helps patients and their families achieve the best possible quality of life during a difficult time.

Issues Addressed in Palliative Care

Cancer is a disease that affects each person differently. The physical as well as emotional effects of cancer, as well as the treatment, can vary and have a significant impact on a person's life.

A palliative care specialist takes into account the unique needs of each patient to provide comprehensive care. They can address a broad range of issues, including physical, emotional, spiritual, caregiver, and practical needs.

The scope and standards of practice in oncology nursing emphasize the importance of a collaborative approach to patient care. The nurse should work in collaboration with the interdisciplinary team, including healthcare providers, pain specialists, and other healthcare professionals, to develop an individualized pain management plan for patients in severe pain. This ensures that the pain is effectively addressed and managed, considering the patient's unique needs and preferences. The collaborative approach promotes holistic care and aligns with evidence-based practices, enhancing the quality of life for patients with advanced cancer.

Physical needs: Palliative care can help alleviate common physical symptoms such as vomiting, pain, loss of appetite, fatigue, nausea, shortness of breath, and insomnia. Palliative care specialists work closely with the patient and the oncology care team to manage these symptoms and improve the patient's comfort.

Emotional and Coping Needs: A cancer diagnosis can cause a range of emotions, including depression, anxiety, and fear. Palliative care specialists can offer resources to help patients and their families deal with emotions. They can provide counseling, support groups, and other services to help people cope with the psychological aspects of cancer.

Spiritual needs: A cancer diagnosis can lead people to search for meaning as well as purpose in their lives. Palliative care specialists can help patients explore their spiritual beliefs and values and find a sense of peace or acceptance. They can offer spiritual counseling, meditation, and other services to help patients address their spiritual needs.

Caregiver needs: Cancer not only affects patients but also their families and caregivers. Caregivers often face challenges such as inadequate social support, uncertainty about how to help their loved one with medical situations, and overwhelming responsibilities. Specialists can help families and friends cope with the extra responsibilities, offer emotional support, and provide education and resources to help them navigate the challenges of caregiving.

Practical needs: Palliative care specialists can assist with financial and legal worries, insurance questions, employment concerns, and other practical needs. They can help patients as well as their families navigate the complex healthcare system while guiding advance directives and the goals of care.

In summary, palliative care is a multidisciplinary approach that aims to improve the quality of life for people living with cancer and other serious illnesses. Palliative care specialists support patients and families coping with serious illness by addressing physical, emotional, spiritual, and practical needs.

Hospice Care

Hospice care is a type of care that concentrates on improving the quality of life for individuals who are facing advanced, life-limiting illnesses, as well as their caregivers. The objective of hospice care is to provide compassionate support for people in the final stages of incurable illness, enabling them to live as comfortably and fully as possible.

Hospice care prioritizes enhancing and affirming life rather than shortening or extending it. It involves symptom management and comfort care rather than trying to cure the underlying disease. To ensure that patients get high-quality care as well as pass away with dignity, a team of healthcare professionals works together.

Hospice care is also centered on the family, involving both the patient and their loved ones in the decision-making process. This approach allows the family to understand the care that is being provided fully and to feel empowered to make informed decisions about end-of-life care.

Starting Hospice Care

When advanced cancer reaches a point where conventional treatments are no longer effective in controlling or curing it, hospice care is employed. Generally, hospice care is recommended for patients with an expected lifespan of about 6 months or less if the illness progresses as expected. Patients with advanced cancer will need to discuss with their doctor and family members when hospice care should be initiated.

Research indicates that hospice care often needs to be initiated early enough. In some cases, patients, family members, or physicians may resist hospice care, believing that it implies "giving up" or that it implies that there is no hope. However, it is important to understand that patients can leave hospice care and resume active cancer treatments if desired. The hope that hospice care brings is a better quality of life, making the most of each day during the advanced stages of illness.

Some physicians may not bring up hospice care, so patients or family members may need to initiate the conversation. If conventional treatments are no longer effective and there are no other treatment options available, discussing hospice care with the doctor or members of the cancer care team is important.

Palliative Care and Symptom Control

Palliative care, also known as supportive care, symptom management, or comfort care, is a type of care given to people who are suffering from a serious illness. Palliative care can be given independently of hospice care, for example, while still receiving treatment for cancer. However, it is often combined with hospice care when cancer is no longer being treated because it has worsened. Palliative care does not treat cancer itself but rather is used to manage symptoms and side effects as early as possible.

Palliative care for hospice patients provides relief from symptoms, pain, and stress. It involves patients and their caregivers in planning care and aims to meet all patient care needs. The palliative care team's specialized professionals help manage mental, physical, emotional, social, and spiritual issues.

Palliative care in hospice is aimed at managing discomfort, pain, and other side effects to help patients enjoy their final stage of life as comfortably as possible while remaining alert to make important decisions.

Home Care and Inpatient Hospice Care

Hospice care is a medical care that is designed to provide comfort and support to individuals who are facing a serious illness or on the verge of the end of their life.

This type of care is typically provided in the home, where the patient can receive personalized attention and support from a team of healthcare professionals.

However, there may be situations where the patient needs to be admitted to a hospital, extended-care facility, or an inpatient hospice center. In these instances, the patient's home hospice team can make the necessary arrangements for inpatient care. The team will stay involved in the patient's care and with their family, provide support and guidance throughout the entire process.

Once the patient is ready to return to their home, they can resume receiving care in the comfort of their surroundings. The home hospice team will continue to provide personalized care and support, ensuring that the patient and their family receive the attention and guidance they need during this difficult time.

Spiritual Care

Spiritual care is a crucial aspect of holistic healthcare that addresses the spiritual and emotional needs of patients. This type of care recognizes that spirituality is an important part of a person's overall well-being and seeks to provide support in a way that is respectful and inclusive of diverse religious beliefs and cultural traditions.

In practice, spiritual care may involve working with a chaplain or other spiritual leader to provide counseling, prayer or meditation sessions, or other forms of emotional support. Some patients may also benefit from assistance in exploring their beliefs about death and dying or in making arrangements for end-of-life rituals or ceremonies that are meaningful to them.

Overall, the goal of spiritual care is to provide patients with the support they need to cope with the emotional as well as spiritual challenges that arise during times of illness or crisis. By addressing the individual needs of each patient, spiritual care can help to promote healing and improve overall quality of life, whatever the outcome of their medical journey may be.

Family Meetings

To keep family members informed about the patient's condition and what to expect, hospice nurses or social workers frequently lead scheduled meetings. These meetings provide an important opportunity for everyone to share their feelings, discuss what's happening and what's needed, and learn about the process of dying and death. These meetings can provide great support and stress relief for family members. Additionally, daily updates may be given informally during routine visits as the nurse or nursing assistant talks with the patient and their caregivers.

Coordination of Care

The hospice team is available always 24/7 to coordinate and supervise all care. They ensure that all involved services share information, including the doctor, the inpatient facility, and other professionals, such as clergy, pharmacists, and funeral directors. If the patient or their caregivers encounter any problems, they are encouraged to contact your hospice team at any time of the day or night. There will always be someone available to assist with whatever arises. Hospice care assures them and their family that they are not alone and that help is available at all times.

Respite Care

Hospice services provide respite care for patients being cared for at home. This care gives friends and family a break from caregiving for up to five days. During this time, the person with cancer is cared for in either a hospice facility or in designated beds in nursing homes or hospitals. Respite care gives families the opportunity to plan a mini-vacation, attend special events, or simply rest while their loved one receives inpatient care.

Bereavement Care

When someone you care about dies, you go through a time of mourning called bereavement. The hospice care team works closely with friends and family who have lost a loved one to help them deal with their grief. A trained volunteer, a clergy member, or a professional counselor can visit, call, or do other things to help the grieving person. Support groups can also help. If it's needed, the hospice team can connect family members and friends who are helping with care with other medical or professional care. Usually, grief support services are available for up to a year after the patient has died.

Hospice Care vs. Palliative Care

Hospice care plus palliative care aim to improve the quality of life as well as ease the symptoms and side effects of people who are seriously ill. In both, there are specialized teams that take care of patients' physical, emotional, mental, social, and spiritual needs. Hospice care and palliative care often go hand in hand, but it's important to remember that they are not the same thing.

How They Are Different

- **When care is given:**

Hospice care is a type of care given to people who are nearing the end of their lives or in the last stages of an illness that can't be cured. It is often given to people whose cancer has spread or is very advanced. Palliative care, on the other hand, is given at any stage of a serious illness. It's meant to make the patient's life better by meeting their mental, physical, and spiritual needs.

- **What other care can be given:**

When there is no active or curative treatment for a serious illness, hospice care is given. "Treatment" in hospice care means taking care of symptoms and side effects. And on the other hand, palliative care can be given while the person is getting active cancer treatment like chemotherapy, radiation, or immunotherapy. To put it more simply, palliative care can be given along with active treatment to help the patient deal with their symptoms and enjoy life more.

- **What the care team does:**

When a patient needs care at the end of their life, a hospice care team takes on the responsibility of coordinating that care. This team communicates with the patient's medical care team to ensure the patient gets the best possible care. On the other hand, a palliative care team is a separate entity that provides care to the patient but does not manage their treatment for the illness. This team communicates with the patient's medical care team to ensure that the patient's overall care is well-coordinated.

Chapter Six: Oncologic Emergencies

Oncologic emergencies can happen at any time during the course of an oncologic diagnosis. As nurses, our overall goals are to identify patients at risk and assess each interaction. Nurses are expected to know how to evaluate a patient's mental and physical health, as well as their health habits and how much they and their family know about the disease and how to treat it. The nurse also checks on the patient's general physical and mental health.

Emergency Situations to Know

A patient with a history of breast cancer presenting to the clinic with complaints of daily retro-orbital headaches that are worse in the morning, and who has severe nausea and vomiting would be given an MRI of the brain. If it reveals multiple metastatic lesions, the patient should be administered Dexamethasone as an initial treatment. Dexamethasone can reduce inflammation, alleviate symptoms, and reduce intracranial pressure, providing immediate relief while further treatment options are considered.

When a patient is experiencing a hypercalcemic crisis, which is life-threatening, a 0.9% saline bolus should be given as the first treatment to correct dehydration and improve renal perfusion, which lowers serum calcium levels.

If your patient with AML has the following lab values: WBC = 86,000, H/H= 8.6/25.1, Plt = 22,000, Cr = 1.8, Na = 132, K = 4.8, Phos = 7.2, LDH = 954, and Uric Acid= 9.5, this patient is experiencing a hypercalcemic crisis, which is life-threatening. A 0.9% saline bolus should be given as the first treatment to correct dehydration and improve renal perfusion, which lowers serum calcium levels.

Radiation therapy can cause a decrease in platelet count, leading to thrombocytopenia. Monitoring for thrombocytopenia is crucial to detect any abnormalities in platelet levels. This allows for timely intervention to prevent bleeding complications.

One of the common complications associated with the use of vascular access devices (VADs) for treatment administration is catheter dislodgement. This refers to the inadvertent movement or removal of the catheter from its intended position. Catheter dislodgement can occur due to patient movement, accidental pulling, or improper securing of the catheter. When a VAD becomes dislodged, it may not function properly or provide reliable access for administering medications or fluids. Prompt action is required to secure or reposition the catheter to prevent complications such as infiltration, infection, or interruption of treatment. Hypertension, hyperglycemia, and visual disturbances are not directly associated with VADs but may be related to the patient's overall health condition or other treatment modalities.

Difficulty breathing, facial swelling, and hives during administration of chemotherapy indicate an immediate and exaggerated immune response. These manifestations are consistent with a Type I hypersensitivity reaction, which is also known as an IgE-mediated hypersensitivity reaction. Exposure to allergens in Type I hypersensitivity triggers histamine and other inflammatory mediator release. This reaction can be life-threatening if not promptly treated with antihistamines, epinephrine, and airway support.

The presence of fever, chills, and fatigue in a patient with low white blood cell count after chemotherapy indicates the risk of infection. In this case, the most appropriate intervention would be to administer a broad-spectrum antibiotic to prevent or treat any potential bacterial infections.

Tumor Lysis Syndrome (TLS)

This is a potential oncologic emergency that can occur during the treatment of certain cancers. Tumor Lysis Syndrome occurs when cancer cells release their contents (such as nucleic acids, potassium, and uric aciD) into the bloodstream following cancer treatment. This release overwhelms the body's ability to eliminate these substances, leading to metabolic imbalances. TLS is most commonly seen in rapidly proliferating hematologic malignancies, such as leukemia and lymphoma. Treatment strategies typically involve aggressive hydration, uric acid-lowering agents, and close monitoring of electrolyte levels.

Disseminated Intravascular Coagulation (DIC)

Cancer patients can develop DIC, a major oncologic emergency. A complicated condition, DIC activates clotting factors throughout the body's small blood arteries, causing blood clots. Organ damage and failure can result from excessive clotting.

Sepsis, trauma, and malignancy often cause DIC. Cancer cells or cancer-related chemicals can enter the bloodstream and activate the clotting system, causing DIC in cancer patients. The mechanisms of DIC in cancer are unknown, but tumor-secreted substances may affect clotting and anticoagulant pathways. The origin and clotting extent of DIC affect its clinical appearance. Patients may experience profuse bleeding, bruising, and petechiae. Shortness of breath, disorientation, and decreased urine production may indicate organ malfunction.

DIC is diagnosed by clinical and laboratory studies. Low platelet count, extended PT and aPTT, increased FDPs, and reduced fibrinogen are common laboratory findings. Imaging tests like ultrasonography or CT scans can detect large organ blood clots. DIC in cancer patients entails addressing the source and correcting irregular clotting, making care difficult. Treatment may involve cancer treatment, supportive care, and anticoagulant medicines to prevent clots. Blood transfusions may be needed to replenish clotting factors or platelets.

DIC prognosis depending on cause and organ damage. Early detection and treatment enhance outcomes. DIC management requires close monitoring of vital signs, laboratory results, and organ function. Effective DIC treatment often requires collaboration with hematologists, oncologists, and critical care doctors.

SEPSIS

Sepsis, which occurs when the body's response to infection damages its tissues and organs, can be fatal. Oncology nurses must be aware of and prepared for this crucial oncologic emergency.

Sepsis occurs when a urinary tract infection or pneumonia spreads to the bloodstream. After infection, the immune system releases chemicals into the bloodstream, causing widespread inflammation. This inflammation can cause a chain of events that harm and impair organs.

Sepsis can cause septic shock, a dramatic blood pressure decline. Septic shock reduces blood flow to essential organs like the brain, heart, and kidneys. Organ failure and death can follow if not addressed immediately.

Sepsis and septic shock symptoms include fever, chills, fast heart rate, rapid breathing, disorientation, and reduced urine output. Improving patient outcomes requires early detection and treatment.

Oncology nurses must regularly monitor patients for sepsis, especially those undergoing cancer therapy, who may have a compromised immune system and be more susceptible to infections. These individuals can avoid sepsis by promptly screening and diagnosing infections.

In sepsis and septic shock, the nurse administers IV fluids to raise blood pressure, starts broad-spectrum antibiotics, and monitors vital signs and organ function. The patient may need vasopressors to support blood pressure or mechanical ventilation to breathe.

In addition, the nurse educates patients and their families about infection symptoms and when to seek medical assistance. Oncology patients can lower sepsis risk by practicing basic hand hygiene, wound care, and infection control.

Hypersensitivity

Hypersensitivity reactions are prevalent in oncologic situations. These reactions occur when the immune system overreacts to cancer drugs. Hypersensitivity reactions can be minor to severe and life-threatening if untreated.

Type I, II, III, and IV hypersensitivity reactions exist. Different immune response mechanisms and symptoms characterize each type.

Immediate hypersensitivity reactions, or type I hypersensitivity reactions, occur quickly after allergen contact. Itching, hives, edema, coughing, and breathing problems are possible. Type I hypersensitivity reactions can cause life-threatening anaphylaxis.

Type II hypersensitivity reactions involve antibody-induced cell or tissue damage. These reactions can cause autoimmune hemolytic anemia or immune thrombocytopenia, where the immune system assaults red blood cells or platelets.

Immune complexes in tissues or blood arteries cause type III hypersensitivity responses. This can cause inflammation and tissue damage, causing joint pain, fever, and rashes. Type III hypersensitivity reactions can cause serum sickness or SLE.

Delayed type IV hypersensitivity reactions develop hours to days following allergen exposure. Inflammation and tissue damage result from T-cell activation in these situations. Type IV hypersensitivity reactions include poison ivy rashes.

Oncology patients with hypersensitivity responses need rapid diagnosis and treatment. This includes halting the suspected cause and treating symptoms with suitable drugs. For milder allergic reactions, antihistamines and corticosteroids may be administered, but epinephrine is usually used.

Oncology nurses must identify and treat cancer patients' hypersensitivity reactions. They must closely monitor patients during therapy and respond rapidly to reactions. These catastrophes can also be prevented and managed by raising awareness of allergies and hypersensitive reactions.

Hypercalcemia

Hypercalcemia is elevated blood calcium. Oncology nurses must be prepared to handle this oncologic emergency.

Cancers that spread to the bone or produce hormones that regulate calcium often cause hypercalcemia. Breast cancer, lung cancer, multiple myeloma, and some leukemias can cause hypercalcemia.

Cancer patients' hypercalcemia is caused by bone metastases. Cancer cells destroy bone, releasing calcium into the bloodstream. Some cancer cells create parathyroid hormone-like chemicals that raise calcium levels.

Hypercalcemia symptoms can vary and be mild. In severe situations, patients may experience fatigue, weakness, nausea, vomiting, constipation, thirst, frequent urination, confusion, and coma. These symptoms must be monitored by oncology nurses for early management to avoid consequences.

To diagnose hypercalcemia, blood tests detect calcium levels. To diagnose the etiology, the patient's medical history, physical exam, and imaging procedures are necessary. The goal of hypercalcemia treatment is to lower calcium levels, relieve symptoms, and find the reason. Hydration is the first-line treatment because it flushes calcium. Intravenous bisphosphonates like zoledronic acid and pamidronate can also slow bone breakdown and reduce calcium. Calcipitonin, corticosteroids, and denosumab are other treatments.

Oncology nurses are vital to hypercalcemia care. They should monitor patients for symptoms, check calcium levels, and help administer treatments. Patients and their family should also learn about hypercalcemia symptoms and when to seek medical assistance.

Cardiac Tamponade

Cardiovascular tamponade is a life-threatening oncologic emergency that requires immediate treatment. The heart is compressed when blood or tumor fluid collects in the pericardial sac. The heart's ability to fill and pump blood is limited by compression, causing hemodynamic instability.

Cancer spreading to the pericardium, the sac around the heart, causes most cardiac tamponade in oncology patients. Infection, trauma, and chest radiation therapy are other causes. It can also result from invasive treatments like central venous catheter implantation or heart surgery. Cardiac tamponade can cause shortness of breath, chest discomfort, low blood pressure, tachycardia, and poor perfusion. Jugular venous distention, distant heart sounds, muffled heart sounds, and pulsusparadoxus may be seen on examination.

Clinical suspicion and echocardiography or CT scans are used to diagnose cardiac tamponade. Echocardiography is useful for detecting pericardial effusion and hemodynamic impairment.

Treating cardiac tamponade entails identifying the source and reducing heart compression. Pericardiocentesis, which drains fluid from the pericardial sac with a needle or catheter, is typically done in emergencies. Pericardial drains can be left in situ to prevent fluid re-accumulation. Surgery to remove a tumor or repair heart damage may be needed to treat cardiac tamponade. To stabilize hemodynamics in the acute phase, intravenous fluids and inotropic drugs may be needed.

Cardiac tamponade prognosis depends on the cause, hemodynamic compromise, and early management. Improving results for this illness requires early detection and treatment.

Chapter Seven: Psychosocial Dimensions of Care

Providing effective, holistic care for patients with cancer demands ability to address both physical and emotional requirements. Psychosocial Dimensions of Oncology Nursing Care explores not only patient problems but also the issues that family and healthcare personnel encounter during the cancer journey. The mental and emotional health of patients and their families is the main focus of psychosocial care. It covers concerns with self-worth, understanding and adjusting to sickness and its aftermath, relationships and social functioning, therapeutic communication, and spiritual well-being.

Psychosocial Distress

Distress can arise due to various factors such as fear of the unknown, uncertainty about prognosis, concerns about treatment outcomes, body image issues, financial burden, changes in roles and relationships, and social isolation. They may face stigma or discrimination from their community or workplace. One important aspect of psychosocial distress is the emotional impact of cancer. Patients often experience a range of emotions including fear, anxiety, sadness, anger, and grief. They may worry about the future and the impact of cancer on their lives. Oncology nurses play a crucial role in providing emotional support, listening to patients' concerns, normalizing their feelings, and helping them cope with their emotions.

Body Image

Physical changes resulting from treatment, such as hair loss, weight gain or loss, and scars, can have a profound effects on patients' self-image. Encouraging the use of prosthetics, wigs, or scarves can help patients regain a sense of normalcy and enhance their self-confidence. Nurses can also employ therapeutic interventions like counseling, support groups, or referrals to mental health professionals to assist patients in managing their emotions and building resilience. It is crucial for oncology nurses to provide education and resources to patients about coping strategies and self-care techniques that can improve body image and self-esteem. Promoting the involvement of supportive family members or friends during the recovery process can also facilitate emotional healing and acceptance.

Anxiety

Anxiety is a common psychosocial distress experienced by individuals, particularly those undergoing cancer treatment. It is characterized by feelings of fear, unease, worry, and nervousness. Oncology nurses play a crucial role in identifying and addressing anxiety in their patients. Understanding the various aspects of anxiety can help nurses provide effective care and support. One important aspect of anxiety is its prevalence among cancer patients.

By recognizing the signs and symptoms of anxiety, nurses can intervene early and provide appropriate interventions. Anxiety can manifest in various ways, including physical symptoms. Patients may experience rapid heartbeat, shortness of breath, trembling, sweating, and gastrointestinal distress. Nurses should be aware of these physical manifestations and inquire about them during patient assessments. By addressing these physical symptoms, nurses can help alleviate the distress experienced by patients.

Loss And Grief

Loss and grief are common experiences in the field of oncology . As an oncology nurse, understanding and addressing these psychosocial dimensions of care is crucial. Loss refers to the experience of being deprived of someone or something of value. In the context of cancer, patients may experience loss in various ways.

This can include loss of physical abilities, loss of independence, loss of self-image, and even loss of life.

Grief, on the other hand, is the emotional response to loss. It is a complex and individual process that can manifest in different ways. Some patients may feel overwhelming sadness, while others may experience anger, guilt, or even numbness. Recognizing and acknowledging the experience of loss and grief is essential for providing holistic care to oncology patients. It is important to create a safe and supportive environment where patients feel comfortable expressing their emotions.

Depression

Depression is a common psychological condition that often accompanies a diagnosis of cancer. It is considered as a psychosocial distress and falls under the psychosocial dimensions of care for an Oncology Nurse. Depression can greatly impact the overall well-being and quality of life of cancer patients. It is crucial for oncology nurses to have a comprehensive understanding of depression in order to effectively support their patients.

Depression, in the context of cancer, is characterized by persistent feelings of sadness, hopelessness, fatigue, and loss of interest in activities. It can affect patients at any stage of the cancer journey, from diagnosis to treatment and survivorship. The causes of depression in cancer patients are multifactorial, including biological, psychological, and social factors. One important aspect of depression to consider is the screening and assessment process. Oncology nurses play a crucial role in identifying patients who may be experiencing depression. This involves using validated screening tools and conducting thorough assessments to determine the severity and impact of depression on the patient's daily life.

Once depression is identified, appropriate interventions can be implemented. Psychosocial support is a key component of managing depression in cancer patients. This may include counseling, psychotherapy, and support groups. Collaborating with other healthcare professionals, such as psychologists and psychiatrists, can further enhance the effectiveness of these interventions. Additionally, education and self-management strategies are vital in empowering patients to cope with depression. Oncology nurses can provide information and resources about depression, its symptoms, and available treatment options. Encouraging patients to engage in self-care activities, such as exercise, relaxation techniques, and maintaining a support network, can also be beneficial.

Loss of Personal Control

Loss of personal control is a significant psychosocial distress experienced by oncology patients. This topic encompasses various aspects that can greatly affect the well-being of individuals undergoing cancer treatment. It involves a loss of autonomy, independence, and self-determination, which can have a profound emotional and psychological impact. One of the primary factors contributing to the loss of personal control is the invasive nature of cancer treatments. Patients often have to undergo surgeries, chemotherapy, radiation therapy, and other invasive procedures, which can leave them feeling helpless and powerless. These interventions disrupt their daily routines, independence, and ability to make decisions about their own bodies.

The loss of of personal control also manifests in the form of treatment-related side effects. Patients may experience symptoms such as pain, fatigue, nausea, and hair loss, which further diminish sense of control over their bodies and their lives. These physical changes can negatively impact their self-image and self-esteem, leading to emotional distress and a loss of confidence. Furthermore, the diagnosis of cancer itself can impose a sense of powerlessness. Patients may feel overwhelmed by the uncertainty of their prognosis, the fear of recurrence, and the potential loss. They may also face the need to rely on others for emotional and practical support, which can challenge their independence and self-sufficiency.

Sexuality

Sexuality is an important aspect of psychosocial care for oncology nurses to address. It encompasses an individual's sexual identity, orientation, desires, and behaviors. Supporting patients in their sexual well-being can positively impact their overall quality of life and emotional well-being during their oncology journey.

One key aspect of sexuality is understanding and respecting each patient's sexual identity. Oncology nurses should recognize that individuals may identify as heterosexual, homosexual, bisexual, or different genders. It is vital to provide a non-judgmental and inclusive environment where patients feel comfortable expressing their sexual orientation.

Another important consideration is the impact of cancer and its treatments on sexual functioning. Many cancer treatments can lead to physical changes in the body, such as surgical scars, changes in body image, or side effects like fatigue and pain, which can affect sexual desire and function. Oncology nurses should be knowledgeable about these potential effects and provide information and support to patients. Communication plays a crucial role in addressing patients' sexual concerns. Oncology nurses should create an open dialogue with patients, allowing them to express their worries and ask questions regarding sexual health. This communication should include discussions about sexual activities, contraception, fertility preservation, and potential concerns related to intimacy and relationships during and after treatment.

Education forms another essential component of addressing sexuality in oncology care. Nurses can provide patients with resources, such as pamphlets or websites that discuss sexual health during and after cancer treatment. These resources should cover topics like managing sexual side effects, counseling services, and support groups available to help patients navigate their sexual concerns.

Counseling and psychological support are crucial for addressing the psychosocial dimensions of sexuality in oncology care. Oncology nurses should identify patients who may benefit from professional counseling to cope with emotional and psychological issues related to their sexual health. This support can help patients improve their self-esteem, body image, and overall well- being.

It's important for oncology nurses to work collaboratively with other healthcare professionals, including oncologists and psychologists, to ensure comprehensive care for patients' sexual concerns. By taking the lead in addressing sexuality, oncology nurses can play a crucial role in enhancing patients' overall well-being and quality of life during their cancer journey.

Reproductive Issues

Reproductive issues are a significant concern for individuals undergoing cancer treatment, and as an oncology nurse, it is crucial to provide comprehensive contraception and fertility preservation. support and guidance in this area. Reproductive issues encompass a range of topics, including diagnosis, treatment plan, and personal preferences.

Contraception is essential for patients of reproductive age who wish to prevent pregnancy during their cancer treatment. It is important to discuss various contraceptive options with patients and their partners, taking into account the potential interactions between contraception and cancer therapy. Barrier methods, such as condoms or diaphragms, are generally safe to use, while hormonal methods like birth control pills or patches may have contraindications or require adjustments in dosage due to potential drug interactions.

For patients interested in preserving their fertility, it is crucial to explore fertility preservation options before starting cancer treatment. This is especially important for patients who may experience fertility-related side effects, such as damage to the ovaries or testes, as a result of certain treatment modalities. Fertility preservation methods include sperm or egg cryopreservation, embryo freezing, or ovarian tissue preservation.

Sexual Dysfunction

Sexual dysfunction refers to difficulties or problems that a person may experience in their sexual life. In the context of oncology, sexual dysfunction can occur as a result of both physical

Physical effects of cancer and its treatment can contribute to sexual dysfunction. For example, certain cancer treatments such as surgery, radiation and psychological effects therapy, and chemotherapy may lead to changes in hormone levels, physical discomfort, or damage to sexual organs. These physical changes can result in pain during intercourse, loss of libido, difficulty achieving or maintaining an erection (erectile dysfunction), or difficulty reaching orgasm. It is important for oncology nurses to address sexual dysfunction in their patients because it can have a profound impact

Psychological effects can also play a significant role in sexual dysfunction among oncology patients. A cancer diagnosis can cause anxiety, depression, body image issues, and stress, which can negatively impact sexual desire and function. Fear of recurrence, relationship changes, and concerns about fertility or sexual attractiveness can further contribute to sexual problems.

Coping Mechanisms and Skills

Coping mechanisms and skills are extremely important for those working in the field of oncology nursing. As oncology nurses provide care and support to patients with cancer, they often witness and experience emotional, psychological, and social challenges. It is vital for these nurses to possess coping mechanisms and skills to deal with the stress and demands of their profession effectively.

One coping mechanism that is crucial for oncology nurses is self-care. Taking care of oneself is essential in maintaining physical and emotional well-being. Engaging in activities that promote relaxation, such as exercise, meditation, or hobbies, can help nurses manage stress and prevent burnout. Additionally, seeking support from friends, family, or professional counselors can provide a valuable outlet for nurses to express their emotions and concerns. Another important coping skill for oncology nurses is effective communication. Being able to communicate with patients, their families, and the healthcare team is vital in providing quality care.

Oncology nurses must develop strong listening and empathetic skills to understand patients' needs and concerns. They should also be able to effectively convey medical information to patients in a compassionate and understandable manner. Resilience is another essential coping mechanism for oncology nurses. It refers to the ability to adapt and bounce back from challenging situations. Resilient nurses are better equipped to handle the emotional ups and downs of providing care to cancer patients. They can maintain a positive attitude, remain focused on their goals, and find meaning in their work, even in the face of adversity.

Furthermore, problem-solving skills are vital for oncology nurses. They often encounter complex situations that require critical thinking and decision-making. Developing effective problem- solving skills allows nurses to assess different situations, identify potential challenges, and find appropriate solutions. This skill helps them navigate difficult situations and provide the best possible care for their patients.

In addition to these coping mechanisms and skills, self-reflection is essential for oncology nurses. Taking time to reflect on their experiences, emotions, and professional growth can enhance self-awareness and promote personal development. It allows nurses to recognize their strengths and weaknesses, make necessary adjustments, and continually improve their practice.

Cultural, Spiritual, and Religious Diversity

Cultural, spiritual, and religious diversity is a critical aspect of providing psychosocial care to oncology patients. As an oncology nurse, it is crucial to understand and respect the diverse cultural backgrounds, spiritual beliefs, and religious practices of each patient. This awareness helps in tailoring care to meet their individual needs and ensure a holistic approach to treatment.

Cultural diversity involves recognizing and appreciating the differences in traditions, customs, values, and beliefs among patients. This includes understanding various languages, dietary needs, and family dynamics. Taking the time to learn about different cultures can enhance communication and foster trust between the nurse and the patient, leading to improved patient outcomes.

Spirituality plays a significant role in the lives of many oncology patients, regardless of their religious affiliation. Some may find solace in their spiritual beliefs, finding strength and meaning in their faith. It is essential for the oncology nurse to be respectful and open-minded, creating a safe space for patients to express their spiritual needs and address any concerns they may have. By encouraging open dialogue, the nurse can provide appropriate resources and support tailored to the patient's spiritual beliefs.

Religious diversity encompasses the different religious affiliations patients may identify with. Understanding the basic practices, rituals, and beliefs of various religions can aid in providing appropriate support and accommodating their needs. This can range from dietary restrictions to scheduling treatments around prayer times or arranging for spiritual leaders to visit patients in the hospital.

Addressing cultural, spiritual, and religious diversity in oncology care also involves recognizing and overcoming potential stereotypes or biases that may impact the quality of care. Patients should feel comfortable and respected, free from discrimination based on their cultural or religious background. By promoting inclusivity and embracing diversity, nurses can create an environment that fosters trust, improves patient satisfaction, and contributes to positive healthcare outcomes.

Financial Concerns

Financial concerns are a significant aspect of the psychosocial dimensions of care for oncology patients. Dealing with a cancer diagnosis can be emotionally and mentally taxing for patients and their families, and financial worries only add to the stress. It is vital for oncology nurses to address these concerns and provide support to help patients navigate through this challenging aspect of their cancer journey.

One of the main financial concerns for cancer patients is the cost of treatment. Cancer treatments, including chemotherapy, radiation therapy, and targeted therapies, can be extremely expensive. Many patients struggle to cover the costs of medications, doctor visits, hospital stays, and other medical expenses. As an oncology nurse, it is essential to be aware of the financial resources available to patients, such as insurance coverage, state and federal assistance programs, and nonprofit organizations that provide financial aid.

Additionally, an oncology nurse should help patients understand their insurance coverage and navigate the complex healthcare system. This involves assisting patients in understanding their insurance benefits, including copays, deductibles, and out-of-pocket expenses. Furthermore, oncology nurses must be knowledgeable about available financial assistance programs and help patients explore potential options.

Transportation costs can also pose a significant financial burden for cancer patients. Many individuals require frequent trips to the hospital or clinic for treatment, which may involve long distances and transportation expenses. It is important for oncology nurses to connect patients with transportation resources, such as local volunteer driver programs or discounted transportation services.

Social Relationships and Family Dynamics

Social relationships and family dynamics play a crucial role in the psychosocial dimensions of care for oncology patients.

These aspects encompass the interactions and support systems within a patient's social circle, including family, friends, and the broader community.

One important aspect of social relationships is the emotional support provided by loved ones. Having a strong support system can significantly impact a patient's psychological well-being throughout their cancer journey. The encouragement, empathy, and understanding from family and close friends can help alleviate anxiety, depression, and feelings of isolation.

Family dynamics also influence the caregiving process. In many cases, family members assume the role of primary caregivers, offering physical and emotional care to the patient. It is vital for oncology nurses to assess the family's dynamics and provide appropriate guidance and support, especially when conflicts or communication breakdowns occur. Supporting the patient's social relationships and family dynamics involves fostering open lines of communication among all parties involved. This can help address conflicts, manage expectations, and ensure everyone understands the patient's needs and wishes. Effective communication is also crucial for ensuring accurate information is shared, enhancing the shared decision-making process.

Maintaining healthy relationships and family dynamics can reduce stress levels for both the patient and their caregivers. Encouraging mutual respect, empathy, and understanding among all members helps create a positive and supportive environment for the patient. This positivity can improve the patient's overall well-being and potentially enhance treatment outcomes.

Understanding cultural and social factors that influence social relationships and family dynamics is also important for oncology nurses. Different cultures may have varying perspectives on illness, caregiving, and family roles. Being sensitive to these differences can help nurses provide appropriate support tailored to each patient's cultural background.

In some cases, cancer may strain social relationships and family dynamics due to the challenges it presents. Role changes, financial burdens, and increased dependency on caregivers can be sources of stress. Oncology nurses must be prepared to address these challenges by offering counseling services, connecting patients and their families with support groups, and providing resources for financial assistance.

Part 2: Practice Tests

Chapter Eight: Practice Test 1

1.   Which of the following is an advantage of an implanted vascular access device over a tunneled central venous catheter?

   A. Decreased risk of infection
   B. Short-term use
   C. Low cost of insertion
   D. Unlimited ability to access

2.   The nurse teaches a patient that the purpose of a living will is to:

   A. Make final decisions regarding treatment until disease progression.
   B. Acknowledge the risks and limitations of recommended therapies.
   C. Appoint a surrogate to make medical decisions.
   D. Establish the patient's desires for care prior to a life-threatening illness.

3.   Within which timeframe will chemotherapy-induced alopecia normally begin after receiving a first treatment?

   A. 24 hours
   B. 1 month
   C. 3 months
   D. 2 weeks

4. A patient with breast cancer who received cyclophospamide five years ago reports a new onset of bruising and fatigue. The nurse suspects:

    A. A Secondary Leukemia.
    B. Liver Failure.
    C. Leukoencephalopathy.
    D. Cardiomyopathy.

5. A patient with a permanent colostomy expresses concern about engaging in sexual intercourse. The nurse first recommends:

    A. Eating immediately before engaging in sexual intercourse.
    B. Having further discussions with a therapist prior to having sexual intercourse.
    C. Tracking bowel habits to best schedule sexual intercourse.
    D. Replacing the ostomy appliance just before engaging in sexual intercourse.

6. A patient with ovarian cancer is most likely to be diagnosed with which of the following secondary malignancies?

    A. Leiomyosarcoma
    B. Gastric carcinoma
    C. Hodgkin lymphoma
    D. Ocular melanoma

7. Which of the following is the best intervention to increase a patient's adherence to taking oral chemotherapy at home?

    A. Calling the patient periodically to monitor for side effects and ask questions
    B. Intructing the patient to double the next dose if a dose is missed
    C. Telling the patient to take over-the-counter medications as needed for nausea
    D. Having the patient pick up a refill at the next appointment if the supply runs out

8. Which of the following risk factors will most significantly increase the risk of developing breast cancer?

    A. Mother diagnosed before age 60
    B. Menopause occuring at age 54
    C. First pregnancy at age 31
    D. Menarche at age 13

9. The nurse teaches a patient that the survivorship care plan is used to:

    A. Provide instructions to the employer to make accomodations upon the return to work.
    B. Provide clear direction for ongoing care and surveillance following treatment.
    C. Take the place of discussions with their oncologist following the completion of treatment.
    D. Replace the patient's electronic medical record.

10. Which of the following is a primary cancer prevention measure?

    A. Testicular self-examination
    B. Guaiac stool test
    C. Postmenopausal estrogen therapy
    D. Sunscreen use

11. A patient with Hodgkin lymphoma is most likely to develop which of the following secondary malignancies?

    A. Colorectal
    B. Melanoma
    C. Leukemia
    D. Ovarian

12. A 19-year-old patient with testicular cancer who will receive cisplatin and pelvic radiation asks if he will be able to conceive children. What should the nurse suggest?

    A. Sexual counseling throughout treatment
    B. Cryopreservation after completing cisplatin treatment
    C. Sildenafil prior to engaging in sexual activity following the completion of treatment
    D. Sperm banking prior to beginning treatment

13. What should a cancer education program for adults with low-literacy levels include?

    A. Multiple forms of the same message and repetition
    B. Medical terms so people become familiar with these words
    C. Frequent use of scored quizzes on new material
    D. Cartoon-type illustrations to explain concepts

14. A patient with intractable dyspnea at the end of life has not experienced any relief with traditional interventions. Which of the following should the nurse next consider?

    A. Asking the physician to increase the doses of all medications
    B. Discussing the initiating of palliative sedation with the team
    C. Calling anesthesia to intubate the patient
    D. Informing the patient that there is nothing else left to give them

15. A patient's adolescent son approaches the nurse about screening for himself. The nurse most appropriately recommends which of the following?

    A. CA 19-9 testing
    B. Prostate-specific antigen testing
    C. Colonoscopy
    D. Testicular self-examination

16.   Which population is most at risk for the undertreatment of pain at the end of life?

    A. Elderly
    B. Men
    C. Obese adults
    D. Young adults

17.   A patient expresses a desire to return back to work following treatment, but still reports significant fatigue. What is the nurse's most appropriate suggestion?

    A. Discussing a flexible work schedule with the employer
    B. Encouraging a delay for an additional year before returning to work
    C. Reflecting on changed roles at home before making a decision
    D. Instructing to avoid discussion of the illness with coworkers

18.   During a home visit, the nurse discovers that a patient has lost 20 pounds since beginning chemotherapy four months ago. What should the nurse do first?

    A. Arrange for Meals on Wheels services
    B. Recommend a high-protein, high-calorie supplement
    C. Consult with the physician
    D. Investigate the cause of weight loss

19.   Neglecting to address a patient's quality of life at the end of life can lead to which of the following?

    A. Hope for recovery
    B. Adequate pain control
    C. Premature death
    D. A sense of peace

20.   The nurse with the ability to recognize and respect differences in beliefs, values, and lifestyles of all patients demonstrates:

    A. Nonmaleficence.

    B. Cultural competence.
    C. Presencing.
    D. Protective buffering.

21.   A 64-year-old African American patient with prostate cancer asks if there is any advice he should give his grown sons regarding prostate screening. The nurse's best response is to recommend shared-decision making for:

    A. A transrectal ultrasound beginning at age 45.
    B. An ultrasound-guided biopsy of the prostate beginning at age 45.
    C. Prostatic acid phosphatase testing beginning at age 45.
    D. Prostate-specific antigen testing beginning at age 45.

22.   A patient with lung cancer will be discharged after receiving etoposide and cisplatin. Discharge instructions should include what information?

    A. A fever should be reported immediately to the physician.
    B. Ringing in the ears is due to the etoposide and will improve in a few days.
    C. Observe the urine carefully for the next two days for blood and immediately report its presence.
    D. Hiccups that develops should be reported immediately to the physician.

23.   Excessive use of smokeless tobacco and alcohol increases the risk for developing which type of cancer?

    A. Hepatocellular
    B. Lung
    C. Laryngeal
    D. Gastric

24.   The use of oral contraceptives for more than five years may provide protection from developing which of the following cancers?

    A. Ovarian
    B. Endometrial
    C. Cervical
    D. Breast

25.   Which of the following medications requires mandatory enrollment in a program to ensure teaching about risks to a fetus is provided?

A. Sorafenib
B. Capecitabine
C. Everolimus
D. Lenalidomide

26.   Advance directives are based upon which of the following principles?

A. Beneficience
B. Autonomy
C. Veracity
D. Justice

27.   What information should the nurse provide to a patient following a loop electrosurgical excision procedure?

A. Avoid inserting anything into the vagina for four weeks.
B. Begin an exercise program to decrease weight gain.
C. Sit upright the majority of the day.
D. Expect extreme fatigue for several months.

28.   Which of the following factors play a major role in the prevention of colon cancer?

A. Acetaminophen
B. Vitamins
C. Diet
D. Exercise

29.   What is the most likely cause of palmar-plantar erythrodysesthesia?

A. Overexposure of fast-growing skin cells
B. Increased circulation during infusion
C. Decreased circulation after infusion
D. Rupture of capillaries from pressure and friction

30. Which of the following is the most appropriate nursing intervention for a patient with cancer who has been informed that treatment has failed?

    A. Offering the patient some time alone to process the news
    B. Reviewing further treatment possibilities offered by the physician
    C. Calling the family in to be with the patient
    D. Asking the patient to share feelings about hearing the news

31. What is the nurse's best response to a patient who asks about the risk of lymphedema following breast-conservation surgery with a sentinel node biopsy and radiation?

    A. "Although your risk is low; precautions still need to be taken."
    B. "If you do not develop lymphedema within the first year, you will not develop it later."
    C. "There is no risk of lymphedema with sentinel node biopsy."
    D. "If you follow the lymphedema guidelines for prevention, you will not develop it."

32. A 28-year-old female patient asks you when it is best to perform a self-breast exam. Your response is the following:

    A. It is best to perform a self-breast exam 7 to 10 days after menses.
    B. It is best to perform a self-breast exam every 6 months on the 1st day of bleeding.
    C. It is best to perform a self-breast exam at the same time every month of the day.
    D. It is best to perform a self-breast exam on the day after ovulation.

33. You are educating a group of young men on preventing testicular cancer. What is a correct statement by a participant regarding a testicular exam?

    A. "The best time to perform a self-exam is after a shower."
    B. "The testicle should feel hard but firm."
    C. "The testicle may have minor lumps or swelling due to monthly hormonal changes."
    D. "I perform a self-testicular exam once every 6 months."

34.   As a shift leader making out patient assignments for the oncoming shift, how would you assign care of a patient that has had a sealed radiation source placed?

    A. You decide to assign the same nurse who had the patient yesterday to continue providing quality care.
    B. You decide to rotate staff and assign a nurse who has not provided care for the patient.
    C. None of the options are correct. Sealed radiation therapy has no special staffing restrictions.
    D. You decide to assign one nurse to care for all the patients undergoing sealed radiation therapy to provide continuum of care.

35.   A patient who has undergone a bone marrow transplant is at greatest risk for what?

    A. Congestive heart failure
    B. Liver failure
    C. HIV
    D. Bleeding and infection

36.   A patient with leukemia is entering the period known as "the nadir". As the nurse, you know the following about this period:

    A. The patient is at greatest risk for bleeding, and the patient can experience a platelet count of 50,000 or less during this period.
    B. The patient is at greatest risk for blood clots, and the patient may experience a platelet count of 500,000 or more.
    C. The patient is at risk for elevated hgb and hct; therefore, are at risk for stroke.
    D. The patient will need to be placed in reverse isolation due to low WBC count.

37. On assessment of a patient with leukemia, how would the patient present clinically?

    A. Elevated hgb and hct, decreased platelets, decreased WBCs, and bradycardia
    B. Decreased hgb and hct, decreased platelets, and elevated or normal WBCs with enlarged lymph nodes
    C. Normal hgb and hct, normal platelets, and increased WBCs
    D. Decreased hgb and hct, increased platelets, and elevated WBCs

38. You are teaching a group of new nurse graduates hired on your oncology unit about oncological disorders. Which statement by a nursing graduate about Hodgkin's disease require re-education?

    A. This disease always presents with hallmark signs of bone pain in the ribs, spine, and pelvis.
    B. Reed Stenberg cells are present in the nodes.
    C. A positive CT scan of liver and spleen presents.
    D. A positive biopsy of the lymph nodes with cervical nodes most often affected.

39. You are developing a plan of care for a patient with multiple myeloma. What nursing intervention(s) would be included in their plan of care?

    A. Assist with coughing and deep breathing exercises.
    B. Apply antiembolic stockings as prescribed.
    C. Encourage at least 2 Liters of fluids per day and skeletal support during moving.
    D. Discuss infertility issues with the patient.

40. Which patient is at highest risk for cervical cancer?

    A. A 21 year old who reports first sexual partner at the age of 14 and that she has had at least 10 sex partners.
    B. A 60-year-old with a history of syphilis and cigarette smoking.
    C. A 32 year old in a monogamous relationship who declined the HPV vaccine.

D. None of the patients are at risk for cervical cancer.

41.   As an oncological nurse, you know what finding is correct regarding breast cancer?

A. Masses are usually felt in the upper outer quadrant beneath the nipple or axilla.
B. Women who've had a late menarche and early menopause are at risk for breast cancer.
C. Nipple retraction is never present.
D. The mass is typically painful and red.

42.   Emma, a 45-year-old oncology nurse, has been working in a busy oncology unit for several years. She has noticed that lately, she feels emotionally drained, experiences a lack of motivation, and finds it increasingly challenging to connect with her patients on an empathetic level. She often finds herself becoming irritable and short-tempered with her colleagues. Which of the following strategies would be most effective for Emma in managing her compassion fatigue?

A. Increase her workload to distract herself from her emotions.
B. Isolate herself from her coworkers to avoid conflict.
C. Engage in regular exercise and physical activity to promote stress relief.
D. Avoid seeking support from her supervisor or colleagues.

43.   Which of the following statements best reflects the concept of culturally congruent care in oncology nursing practice?

A. Providing standard care without considering cultural differences.
B. Implementing evidence-based practice guidelines regardless of cultural beliefs.
C. Tailoring care to meet the unique cultural needs and values of the patient.
D. Promoting assimilation of patients into the dominant cultural practices.

44. Mrs. Johnson, a 55-year-old breast cancer patient, has been undergoing chemotherapy and radiation therapy for the past three months. She is experiencing significant side effects, including nausea, vomiting, and fatigue. The physician has recommended an antiemetic medication to manage her symptoms. What is the role of the oncology-certified nurse in this situation?

    A. Administer the antiemetic medication to Mrs. Johnson at the prescribed times.
    B. Instruct Mrs. Johnson on the importance of taking the antiemetic medication regularly.
    C. Collaborate with the healthcare team to develop a comprehensive care plan for Mrs. Johnson.
    D. Educate Mrs. Johnson about potential side effects and self-care measures to alleviate symptoms.

45. Which of the following is an example of a targeted therapy used in the treatment of cancer?

    A. Chemotherapy drugs
    B. Radiation therapy
    C. Hormone therapy
    D. Surgery

46. Sarah, a 45-year-old patient diagnosed with advanced-stage lung cancer, has been receiving chemotherapy for the past six months. During a routine check-up, Sarah's oncologist discovers that her cancer has progressed further, and she only has a few months left to live. Sarah's family, who are not aware of the recent findings, insist on pursuing a more aggressive treatment plan to extend her life. As an Oncology Certified Nurse, what should be your response in this situation?

    A. Share the recent findings with Sarah's family and discuss the implications of the aggressive treatment plan.
    B. Respect Sarah's autonomy and inform her about the recent findings, allowing her to make an informed decision.

C. Convince Sarah's family that the aggressive treatment plan will only cause more harm and recommend palliative care options.
D. Keep the recent findings confidential and carry on with the aggressive treatment plan as per the family's request.

47. Linda is a 65-year-old patient undergoing immunotherapy for advanced melanoma. During her therapy session, she developed a sudden and severe rash, difficulty breathing, and swelling around her face and lips. The nurse suspects an allergic reaction to the immunotherapy drug. Which of the following actions should the nurse take first?

A. Administering an antihistamine medication
B. Assessing Sarah's vital signs and respiratory status
C. Continuing the immunotherapy treatment as scheduled
D. Documenting the reaction for future reference

48. A patient with advanced lung cancer is experiencing dyspnea and tachypnea. Which of the following interventions should the nurse prioritize to assist with symptom management?

A. Administering supplemental oxygen
B. Encouraging deep breathing exercises
C. Administering corticosteroids
D. Encouraging frequent rest periods

49. Mrs. Smith, a 55-year-old female, is diagnosed with breast cancer. She undergoes surgery to remove the tumor, followed by chemotherapy. During the nursing assessment, the nurse noted that Mrs. Smith had developed neutropenia. Which of the following statements accurately explains the pathophysiology of neutropenia in cancer patients?

A. Neutropenia occurs due to bone marrow suppression caused by chemotherapy and radiation therapy.
B. Neutropenia results from the tumor invading the bone marrow and inhibiting neutrophil production.
C. Neutropenia is a side effect of hormone therapy commonly used to treat breast cancer.

    D. Neutropenia occurs due to the release of toxic substances by tumor cells that damage bone marrow.

50.   Mr. Anderson, a 60-year-old patient with lung cancer, is receiving chemotherapy as part of his treatment. He has been experiencing nausea and vomiting after each chemotherapy session, affecting his overall quality of life. His family suggests using complementary and alternative medicine (CAM), such as ginger and acupuncture, to manage these symptoms. What is the nurse's responsibility in this situation?

    A. Dismiss the family's suggestions and focus on conventional medical interventions for symptom management.
    B. Encourage the family to explore CAM options to alleviate the patient's symptoms.
    C. Conduct a literature review on the effectiveness of ginger and acupuncture in managing nausea and vomiting caused by chemotherapy.
    D. Refer the patient to a CAM specialist for further evaluation and treatment.

51.   Sarah, a 45-year-old female with a history of breast cancer, presents to the emergency department with new-onset lower back pain and weakness in both of her legs. She also reports recent bladder and bowel incontinence. On physical examination, there is a bilateral lower-extremity weakness with decreased sensation below the level of T10. An MRI reveals spinal cord compression at the level of T10. What is the most appropriate nursing intervention for Sarah?

    A. Administer opioid analgesics for pain relief
    B. Assist the patient with ambulation to promote mobility
    C. Apply ice packs to the affected area to reduce inflammation
    D. Initiate immediate radiation therapy to relieve spinal cord compression

52.   Which of the following mechanisms is responsible for the development of cervical cancer?

    A. Chronic inflammation
    B. Tumor suppressor gene activation

C. Overexpression of HER2/neu receptor

D. Insulin resistance

53. A blood and bone marrow transplant (BMT) is a treatment option for certain types of cancer and blood disorders. Which of the following statements about BMT is correct?

   A. BMT is a type of surgical procedure that involves the removal and replacement of the entire bone marrow.
   B. BMT is primarily used in the treatment of solid tumors and does not involve the use of stem cells.
   C. BMT can be performed using the patient's healthy cells (autologous transplant) or cells from a donor (allogeneic transplant).
   D. BMT is only effective in the treatment of hematological malignancies, not non-malignant blood disorders.

54. Which nursing intervention is most appropriate for a patient with impaired mobility due to musculoskeletal alterations?

   A. Encouraging bed rest to prevent further strain on the affected area
   B. Assisting with range of motion exercises to maintain joint flexibility
   C. Administering muscle relaxants to relieve pain
   D. Providing heat therapy to alleviate muscle stiffness

55. Emily is a 45-year-old patient diagnosed with advanced-stage ovarian cancer. She has undergone multiple rounds of chemotherapy and surgery but shows no signs of improvement. Lately, she has been expressing feelings of hopelessness despair, and Questioning her beliefs. During a routine assessment, the nurse observes that Emily is experiencing spiritual distress. What is the most appropriate nursing intervention to address Emily's spiritual distress?

   A. Refer Emily to a support group for cancer survivors.
   B. Discuss the possibility of participating in a religious ceremony.
   C. Encourage Emily to journal her thoughts and feelings.
   D. Provide Emily with information about palliative care services.

56. Mrs. Thomas, a 60-year-old female, has been admitted to the oncology unit for the management of advanced ovarian cancer. On the third day of her hospitalization, she complained of severe abdominal pain, nausea, and vomiting. Physical examination reveals abdominal distention with decreased bowel sounds. Mrs. Thomas has not passed stool for the past 48 hours. Lab results are within normal limits, except for a mild leukocytosis. What is the most appropriate nursing intervention for Mrs. Thomas?

    A. Administer antiemetics and initiate a clear liquid diet
    B. Prepare the client for a surgical procedure to relieve the obstruction
    C. Administer laxatives and increase fluid intake
    D. Administer pain medications and document the findings

57. Which of the following strategies can be helpful in managing fatigue in cancer patients?

    A. Avoiding physical activity
    B. Consuming high amounts of caffeine
    C. Implementing relaxation techniques
    D. Maintaining irregular sleep patterns

58. Mrs. Anderson, a 65-year-old breast cancer survivor, has been experiencing deep bone pain. The healthcare provider suspects the possibility of bone metastasis due to her previous history of breast cancer. Which of the following is a common location for bone metastasis in breast cancer patients?

    A. Humerus
    B. Femur
    C. Radius
    D. Tibia

59. Which of the following statements best describes the role of the oncology-certified nurse in providing end-of-life care?

    A. Collaborating with the interdisciplinary team to develop a comprehensive care plan.

B. Administering high doses of pain medication to ensure patient comfort.

C. Encouraging patients to pursue aggressive treatment options.

D. Focusing solely on the physical needs of the patient.

60. A patient demonstrates an adequate understanding of the teaching provided regarding chemotherapy and Myelosuppression by stating: "Myelosuppression is:

A. A potential side effect of many cancer treatments."

B. Unintentional prior to a bone marrow transplant."

C. When laboratory values show an elevation in the white blood cell count."

D. The overreaction of the body's immune system to a medication."

61. Alkylating agents exert their effects by:

A. Causing the release of toxic free radicals inside the cell, triggering cell apoptosis.

B. Attaching to CD52 on the surface of B and T cells, resulting in antibody-dependent lysis.

C. Disrupting metabolic processes that depend on folate, which are essential for cell replication.

D. Binding to DNA strands, preventing DNA replication and cell division.

62. The nurse preparing to instill intravesical mitomycin should wear which of the following pieces of personal protective equipment?

A. A pair of shoe covers

B. A plastic face shield

C. A front-closing laboratory gown

D. One pair of powdered nitrile gloves

63. Adjuvant therapy for breast cancer is administered:

A. Before primary therapy to shrink a tumor that is inoperable in its current state.

B. At any time during therapy to cure the patient and kill cancer cells.

    C. To locally treat cancer with minimal harm to normal cells.

    D. In order to increase the chances of long-term survival without the disease recurring, primary therapy must be undergone.

64. Hormone therapy is effective for which two types of cancer?

    A. Sarcoma and small-cell lung

    B. Lymphoma and gallbladder

    C. Breast and prostate

    D. Liver and chronic myeloid leukemia

65. A 25-year-old patient is being treated with temozolomide. The patient is instructed to:

    A. Take the medication at bedtime on an empty stomach.

    B. Divide the medication doses over 24 hours.

    C. Consume a magnesium supplement with the medication.

    D. Ingest the medication with a full glass of milk.

66. Which of the following chemotherapy orders should the nurse question?

    A. Intramuscular asparaginase

    B. Intraperitoneal cisplatin

    C. Subcutaneous bortezomib

    D. Intrathecal vincristine

67. Which of the following conditions will most likely be treated by an allogeneic stem cell transplant?

    A. Chronic myeloid leukemia

    B. Hodgkin lymphoma

    C. Multiple myeloma

    D. Follicular thyroid cancer

68.   When does nadir typically occur after the completion of a chemotherapy treatment cycle?

A. 3 weeks
B. 1 - 3 days
C. 7 - 10 days
D. 5 weeks

69.   Myeloablative conditioning for stem cell transplantation includes:

A. High-dose chemotherapy.
B. A nutritional analysis.
C. A retrograde surgical intervention.
D. A fitness evaluation.

70.   Information about which of the following side effects should be provided to a patient being treated with posaconazole?

A. Torsades de Pointes
B. Pancreatitis
C. Toxic epidermal necrolysis
D. Aplastic anemia

71.   Surgery is a cancer treatment modality that:

A. Aims to remove only a portion of the primary tumor.
B. It is only used as a palliative measure to relieve symptoms.
C. It causes less toxicity when used in conjunction with chemotherapy.
D. It may be the only treatment that a patient requires.

72.   The nurse is teaching a patient about discharge medications following a hematopoietic stem cell transplant. The nurse explains that the purpose of tacrolimus is to prevent:

A. Sinusoidal obstruction syndrome.
B. Viral pneumonia.
C. Fungal pneumonia.

D. Graft-versus-host disease.

73.   A patient with breast cancer who is 14 weeks pregnant presents for treatment prior to beginning chemotherapy. She is concerned about the potential treatment effects on her baby. What information should the nurse provide to the patient?

    A. A spontaneous abortion will most likely occur.
    B. Chemotherapy given after the first trimester has minimal fetal toxicities.
    C. Doses will be decreased to ensure safety.
    D. Treatment will be held until after the delivery of the child.

74.   A patient with an unresectable T2 N2 M1 adenocarcinoma of the colon is receiving fluorouracil and leucovorin. What is the goal of this treatment regimen?

    A. Promote cellular transformation
    B. Control cancer cell growth
    C. Increase cellular contact inhibition
    D. Promote radiosensitivity

75.   Which diseases are treated with allogeneic stem cell transplants?

    A. Acute lymphoblastic leukemia
    B. Breast cancer
    C. Germ cell tumors
    D. Amyloidosis

76.   What is the primary goal of radiation therapy for muscle-invasive bladder cancer?

    A. Preserve the function of the bladder
    B. Prevent further spread of disease to the brain
    C. Prepare the body for chemotherapy
    D. Minimize the time to surgery

77. Which medication is most likely to cause oral mucositis?

    A. Dexamethasone
    B. Interleukin-2
    C. Rituximab
    D. Fluorouracil

78. Which of the following is a risk factor for treatment-related pneumonitis?

    A. Mantle field radiation
    B. Concomitant use of steroids
    C. Less than 60 years of age
    D. Oxygen therapy at low concentrations

79. Asparaginase has demonstrated a clinical response for patients with which of the following diagnoses?

    A. Non-small lung cancer
    B. Acute lymphocytic leukemia
    C. Cutaneous T-cell lymphoma
    D. Hairy-cell leukemia

80. The nurse counsels a 32-year-old patient with breast cancer and her partner about contraception prior to initiating chemotherapy. Which of the following statements by the patient indicates an adequate understanding of the recommendations?

    A. "I do not need to worry about birth control while receiving chemotherapy."
    B. "I must agree to use birth control pills or a reliable barrier method as recommended by my physician."
    C. "Hormone pills are the easiest and safest method of birth control."
    D. "I will call my gynecologist to discuss having my tubes tied."

81. What is an indicator that a patient scheduled to receive oxaliplatin needs additional teaching?

    A. "I will call the triage number if I develop a fever."

B. "I have already ordered a wig so that I can match my hair color."

C. "I am scheduled to get my flu shot before I start my chemotherapy."

D. "To prevent mouth sores, I am going to eat ice chips while I receive chemotherapy."

82. The nurse teaches a patient receiving intraperitoneal cisplatin to expect:

A. Frequent position changes while the medication is administered.

B. To travel to the operating room to receive the medication under fluoroscopy.

C. The medication is to be cold and to experience significant pain.

D. Take nothing by mouth for 12 hours prior to treatment.

83. Epidermal growth factor receptor inhibitors work inside the cell to:

A. Produce antibodies that recognize and destroy cancer cells.

B. Activate T cells to mount an attack on the immune system on cancer cells.

C. Block binding on the intracellular portion of the receptor.

D. Promote the proliferation of nonmalignant cells to repair the body.

84. A chimeric monoclonal antibody is a combination of mouse and:

A. Horse antibodies.

B. Cow antibodies.

C. Human antibodies.

D. Plant antibodies.

85. The rationale for administering whole breast radiation following a lumpectomy for a patient with stage I breast cancer is to remove:

A. Microscopic disease.

B. Metastatic disease.

C. Locally advanced disease.

D. Nodal disease.

86.   A patient with a tumor on the floor of the mouth is receiving a course of radiation therapy. The nurse should advise the patient to:

   A. Avoid consuming alcohol.
   B. Avoid using topical anesthetics.
   C. Consume one liter of fluid daily.
   D. Apply spices to food.

87.   Intravenous fluids containing sodium bicarbonate are administered to patients receiving high-dose methotrexate to:

   A. Protect against hyperuricemia.
   B. Eliminate the need for a leucovorin rescue.
   C. Maintain alkaline urine.
   D. Reduce the risk of a hypersensitivity reaction.

88.   In what kind of medicine does blocking ligand-receptor activation and immune modulation mess with cell membrane-bound targets?

   A. Alkylating agent
   B. Monoclonal antibody
   C. Vascular endothelial growth factor
   D. Antitumor antibiotic

89.   Which of the following medications is known to be carcinogenic?

   A. Streptozocin
   B. Mitoxantrone
   C. Dacarbazine
   D. Etoposide

90. Jane, a 55-year-old woman, is undergoing palliative care for advanced breast cancer with bone metastasis. She complains of increasing difficulty in performing her routine activities of daily living (ADLs) due to weakness and fatigue. As her oncology nurse, you understand that alterations in functioning related to cancer and its treatment can significantly impact a patient's quality of life. Which of the following interventions would be most appropriate for managing Jane's alterations in functioning?

    A. Encouraging Jane to engage in regular physical exercise
    B. Administering a high-dose opioid analgesic to alleviate her pain
    C. Suggesting adaptive equipment to assist with ADLs
    D. Recommending cognitive behavioral therapy to address psychological distress

91. Which of the following complications is commonly associated with blood and marrow transplant (BMT)?

    A. Hypertension
    B. Diabetes mellitus
    C. Graft-versus-host disease (GVHD)
    D. Asthma

92. Which of the following is an appropriate non-pharmacological intervention for managing pain in cancer patients?

    A. Administering opioids
    B. Applying heat or cold packs
    C. Increasing the dosage of analgesics
    D. Using transcutaneous electrical nerve stimulation (TENS)

93. Sarah, a 42-year-old female with stage IV non-small cell lung cancer (NSCLC), has been prescribed the targeted therapy Erlotinib (Tarceva). During a follow-up visit, the nurse assesses Sarah and notes that her skin is dry and itchy. Which of the following nursing interventions is most appropriate for managing this side effect?

    A. Apply a high-potency topical corticosteroid.

B. Instruct the patient to avoid using any moisturizers.

C. Perform frequent skin assessments to monitor for further complications.

D. Administer oral antihistamines to alleviate the itching.

94. Which chronic side effect is associated with hormone therapy in breast cancer patients?

   A. Alopecia
   B. Osteoporosis
   C. Nephrotoxicity
   D. Pulmonary fibrosis

95. Mary is a 45-year-old woman diagnosed with breast cancer. She is undergoing treatment and experiencing several financial concerns due to the high cost of cancer care. She has a limited income and is worried about how to manage her medical bills, medications, and other healthcare expenses. As an Oncology Certified Nurse, which of the following interventions would be most appropriate for addressing Mary's financial concerns?

   A. Suggest Mary consider taking out a loan to cover the medical expenses.
   B. Refer Mary to a financial counselor who can provide information on assistance programs.
   C. Advise Mary to stop her cancer treatment to reduce the financial burden.
   D. Encourage Mary to rely solely on her health insurance coverage for managing her expenses.

96. Sarah, a 65-year-old female, is admitted to the oncology unit with a diagnosis of brain metastasis. She is experiencing severe headaches, difficulty with coordination, and changes in her level of consciousness. On examination, the nurse notes papilledema and signs of increased intracranial pressure. Which of the following interventions should the nurse prioritize for Sarah?

   A. Administering a pain medication to manage her headaches
   B. Monitoring her vital signs every 4 hours

C. Assisting with range-of-motion exercises to improve coordination

D. Elevating the head of the bed to promote venous drainage

97. Which statement about cultural, spiritual, and religious diversity is correct?

A. All patients from the same cultural background have the same beliefs and practices.

B. Nurses should disregard cultural and religious beliefs when providing care.

C. Understanding cultural, spiritual, and religious beliefs can enhance patient-centered care.

D. Cultural, spiritual, and religious diversity has no impact on patient outcomes.

98. What is the primary role of a support group for cancer patients?

A. Administering medication and providing medical treatments.

B. Offering financial assistance and insurance support.

C. Facilitating peer interaction and emotional support.

D. Assisting with nutrition and dietary planning.

99. Martha is a 65-year-old woman who has been receiving chemotherapy for breast cancer. She complains of persistent fatigue and low energy levels. The nurse assesses her fatigue level using the Wong-Baker Faces Pain Rating Scale. Martha rates her fatigue as a 7 out of 10. The nurse educates her about fatigue management strategies, including pacing her activities, balancing rest and exercise, and maintaining a healthy diet. Which statement made by Martha indicates a need for further education?

A. "I should try to push myself to do more even if I feel tired."

B. "I will make sure to include protein-rich foods in my diet."

C. "I will take short naps during the day to help alleviate fatigue."

D. "I will ask my doctor about adjusting my medication dosage."

100.   A 55-year-old female patient, Mrs. Johnson, is diagnosed with breast cancer, and her oncologist recommends molecular testing for genetic mutations. The patient is worried and asks the nurse about the purpose of this test. How should the nurse respond?

   A. "Molecular testing helps to identify genetic mutations that increase the risk of developing certain types of cancer."
   B. "Molecular testing is used to determine the stage of cancer and plan appropriate treatment strategies."
   C. "Molecular testing assists in assessing the response to chemotherapy and monitoring disease progression."
   D. "Molecular testing is performed to identify potential side effects of cancer treatment."

101.   Jane is a breast cancer survivor who recently completed her treatment. She has been offered a job promotion, but she is hesitant to accept it due to concerns about potential discrimination. Which of the following statements is true regarding discrimination concerns for cancer survivors?

   A. Cancer survivors are protected from discrimination under the Americans with Disabilities Act (ADA).
   B. Cancer survivors are not at risk of facing discrimination in the workplace.
   C. Cancer survivors should not disclose their cancer history to avoid discrimination.
   D. Cancer survivors cannot pursue legal action if they experience discrimination.

102.   Which of the following interventions can help address spiritual distress in individuals?

   A. Assisting the individual in exploring personal values and beliefs.
   B. Prescribing medications for anxiety relief.
   C. Encouraging avoidance of spiritual discussions.
   D. Focusing solely on physical symptoms.

103. Mark, a 60-year-old man, is undergoing chemotherapy for the treatment of lung cancer. He is concerned about the causes of cancer and asks his nurse about the role of environmental factors in carcinogenesis. What would be the nurse's best response?

    A. "Environmental factors have no influence on carcinogenesis."
    B. "Environmental factors play a minor role in the development of cancer."
    C. "Environmental factors are major contributors to carcinogenesis."
    D. "Carcinogenesis is solely determined by genetic factors."

104. Emily, a 50-year-old patient, has been recently diagnosed with stage III breast cancer. The oncology nurse is discussing the patient's treatment plan, and the importance of epidemiology is emphasized. The nurse explains that epidemiology in oncology primarily focuses on:

    A. Identifying and managing risk factors for cancer development.
    B. Administering chemotherapy and radiation therapy to patients.
    C. Educating patients about self-breast examination techniques.
    D. Providing emotional support to patients and their families.

105. Mr. Anderson, a 60-year-old patient with multiple myeloma, is receiving chemotherapy. During a routine assessment, the nurse observes petechiae and ecchymosis on the patient's skin. Upon further investigation, laboratory results reveal a platelet count of 40,000/mm3. What intervention should the nurse implement?

    A. Initiate bleeding precautions.
    B. Administer a platelet transfusion.
    C. Apply cold compresses to the affected areas.
    D. Encourage the patient to avoid physical activity.

106. Which complementary and integrative modality involves the use of fine needles inserted into specific points on the body to improve energy flow and alleviate symptoms?

    A. Massage therapy
    B. Acupuncture

C. Herbal supplements

D. Meditation

107. Sarah, a 45-year-old breast cancer survivor, recently completed her treatment and is concerned about the possibility of cancer recurrence. She asks the nurse about the signs and symptoms she should be aware of. Which of the following options should the nurse provide to address Sarah's concerns?

   A. Changes in breast appearance or shape.
   B. Persistent cough or hoarseness.
   C. Headaches or frequent dizziness.
   D. Pain or tenderness in the lower back.

108. Mrs. Parker, a 45-year-old breast cancer survivor, recently completed her treatment and is ready to return to work. She is concerned about how her cancer history will affect her employment opportunities. She contacts her oncology nurse for advice on disclosing her medical condition to potential employers. The nurse explains that:

   A. Mrs. Parker should disclose her cancer history during the interview to build trust and show transparency.
   B. Mrs. Parker should not disclose her cancer history unless required by law or if it directly affects her ability to perform the job.
   C. Mrs. Parker should disclose her cancer history after she has been offered the job to ensure fair treatment from her employer.
   D. Mrs. Parker should consult an attorney before deciding whether to disclose her cancer history during the job application process.

109. Michael, a 60-year-old man with prostate cancer, is experiencing erectile dysfunction as a result of his treatment. He is feeling distressed and believes that his sexual relationship with his spouse is permanently damaged. Which of the following nursing interventions would be most appropriate in this situation?

   A. Dismissing Michael's concerns as a normal part of aging and advising him to accept the changes.

B. Suggesting Michael seek alternative sexual partners to fulfill his sexual needs.

C. Assisting Michael and his spouse in exploring other non-sexual ways to foster intimacy and emotional connection.

D. Encouraging Michael to engage in sexual activities despite the erectile dysfunction as a means of maintaining a strong bond with his spouse.

110. Susan, a 52-year-old breast cancer survivor, completed her chemotherapy and radiation treatments six months ago. She has been experiencing persistent fatigue and weakness since then. Susan's oncology nurse referred her to a rehabilitation specialist to address her concerns. During the assessment, the rehabilitation specialist evaluated Susan's muscle strength, endurance, and functional mobility. Based on the assessment findings, the specialist recommends a tailored exercise program for Susan. Which of the following statements about cancer rehabilitation is accurate?

A. Cancer rehabilitation-only focuses on managing pain and discomfort.

B. Cancer rehabilitation is not necessary after completing cancer treatments.

C. Cancer rehabilitation aims to improve cancer survivors' overall quality of life.

D. Cancer rehabilitation is only beneficial if started during active cancer treatment.

111. Mark, a 60-year-old prostate cancer survivor, recently underwent prostatectomy surgery. He is concerned about the potential impact of the surgery on his sexual function and wants to explore rehabilitation options. Mark's oncology nurse introduces him to the concept of penile rehabilitation and explains its benefits. Which of the following statements about penile rehabilitation after prostatectomy is accurate?

A. Penile rehabilitation is not effective in restoring erectile function after prostatectomy.

B. Penile rehabilitation mainly focuses on improving urinary continence after prostatectomy.

C. Penile rehabilitation involves the use of medications to treat post-prostatectomy erectile dysfunction.

D. Penile rehabilitation typically starts immediately after prostatectomy surgery.

112. Which non-pharmacologic comfort measure should be prioritized for promoting emotional support in a patient receiving end-of-life care?

   A. Physical therapy
   B. Music therapy
   C. Antibiotic therapy
   D. Oxygen therapy

113. Which of the following is an example of a therapeutic communication technique used in oncology nursing practice?

   A. Providing reassurance and empathy
   B. Minimizing expressions of emotion
   C. Focusing on healthcare provider's perspective
   D. Interrupting the patient while speaking

114. Mrs. Johnson, a 65-year-old female, visits an oncology nurse for a routine check-up. She has a family history of breast cancer, with her mother being diagnosed at the age of 60. Mrs. Johnson is concerned about her own risk of developing breast cancer. Which of the following statements about non-modifiable risk factors for breast cancer is true?

   A. Being 65 years old increases Mrs. Johnson's risk of breast cancer.
   B. Mrs. Johnson's gender increases her risk of breast cancer.
   C. Mrs. Johnson's family history increases her risk of breast cancer.
   D. All non-modifiable risk factors can be eliminated.

115. Mr. Anderson, a 30-year-old male, has recently been diagnosed with colorectal cancer. He is concerned about the factors that may have contributed to his diagnosis. Which of the following statements about non-modifiable risk factors for colorectal cancer is true?

   A. Mr. Anderson's age increases his risk of colorectal cancer.
   B. Mr. Anderson's gender increases his risk of colorectal cancer.
   C. Mr. Anderson's genetic factors can modify his risk of colorectal cancer.

D. All non-modifiable risk factors for colorectal cancer are related to life-style choices.

116. Ms. Thomas, a 45-year-old female, is undergoing chemotherapy for stage III breast cancer. She presents with a low absolute neutrophil count (ANC) of 500 cells/mmł, putting her at risk for infection. Which statement regarding neutrophils is accurate?

A. Neutrophils are the most numerous types of white blood cells.
B. Neutrophils primarily function in humoral immunity.
C. Neutrophil count increases during acute viral infections.
D. Neutrophils release histamine to promote vascular dilation.

117. Mr. Johnson, a 50-year-old man diagnosed with prostate cancer, is worried about the financial burden his treatment might impose on his family. He has private health insurance coverage but is concerned about additional expenses not covered by his policy. Which of the following interventions by the oncology nurse would be most appropriate for addressing Mr. Johnson's concerns?

A. Advise Mr. Johnson to avoid informing his insurance company about his cancer diagnosis to prevent policy changes.
B. Encourage Mr. Johnson to rely on crowdfunding platforms to raise funds for his treatment.
C. Collaborate with a social worker to explore financial assistance programs and resources available to Mr. Johnson.
D. Suggest Mr. Johnson forego cancer treatment due to potential financial burdens on his family.

118. Which of the following is an essential component of culturally congruent care in oncology nursing practice?

A. Enforcing the dominant cultural norms and practices on the patient.
B. Minimizing the involvement of family members in the care decision-making process.
C. Using standardized assessment tools without considering cultural diversity.

D. Acknowledging and respecting the unique cultural perspectives and values of the patient.

119. Mrs. Johnson, a 78-year-old terminally ill patient with metastatic lung cancer, resides in a long-term care facility. Her family expresses concern about her increased pain levels and requests stronger pain medication. The nurse should:

   A. Assess Mrs. Johnson's pain and consult with the healthcare provider for a potential change in pain medication.
   B. Explain to the family that increasing the pain medication could lead to adverse effects.
   C. Encourage the family to consider non-pharmacological pain management interventions.
   D. Disregard the family's concerns as part of the disease progression.

120. Mr. Thomas, a 63- year-old male with lung cancer, is receiving his immunotherapy treatment. Shortly after the infusion of pembrolizumab, he developed pruritus, facial swelling, and throat tightness. His blood pressure is 150/90 mmHg, his heart rate is 100 beats per minute, and he is coughing. What is the most appropriate nursing intervention?

   A. Administer diphenhydramine intravenously.
   B. Initiate cardiopulmonary resuscitation (CPR).
   C. Discontinue the infusion immediately.
   D. Administer nebulized bronchodilators.

121. Which of the following interventions should the nurse prioritize for a patient experiencing radiation-induced dermatitis?

   A. Applying corticosteroid creams.
   B. Using hot water for bathing.
   C. Wearing tight-fitting clothing.
   D. Using mild soap and patting skin dry gently.

122. Which of the following may affect the approval of insurance claims for cancer treatment?

    A. The type of cancer
    B. Age of the patient
    C. Pre-existing medical conditions
    D. The employment status of the patient

123. Mrs. Johnson, a 68-year-old patient with advanced lung cancer, is receiving palliative care for symptom management. She is experiencing dyspnea and anxiety. The most appropriate nursing intervention for Mrs. Johnson's dyspnea and anxiety would be:

    A. Administering high-flow oxygen therapy.
    B. Providing pharmacological interventions such as opioids.
    C. Encouraging relaxation techniques and deep breathing exercises.
    D. Initiating continuous positive airway pressure (CPAP).

124. Mrs. Anderson, a 58-year-old female with breast cancer, is receiving her scheduled chemotherapy. During the administration of paclitaxel, she suddenly developed dyspnea, wheezing, and a rapid onset of generalized urticaria. Her blood pressure is 80/50 mmHg, her heart rate is 120 beats per minute, and she appears anxious and restless. What is the most appropriate initial nursing action?

    A. Administer epinephrine intramuscularly.
    B. Maintain a patent airway and administer oxygen.
    C. Administer a H1 antihistamine intravenously.
    D. Administer a corticosteroid intravenously.

125. Which intervention is most appropriate for a patient experiencing a loss of personal control in an oncology setting?

    A. Encouraging the patient to make decisions regarding their care.
    B. Administering medications without discussing them with the patient.
    C. Restricting the patient's access to information about their condition.
    D. Making decisions for the patient without their input.

126. Oncologic emergencies can happen at any time during the course of an oncologic diagnosis. As nurses, our overall goals are to:

   A. Prevent, reverse or minimize life-threatening complication.
   B. Identify patients at risk and assess each interaction.
   C. Educate patients and family members regarding risk and how or when to manage the complications.
   D. Follow the physician's orders only.

127. Your patient with AML has the following lab values: WBC = 86,000, H/H= 8.6/25.1, Plt = 22,000, Cr = 1.8, Na = 132, K = 4.8, Phos = 7.2, LDH = 954, and Uric Acid= 9.5 Based on this information, what medication would you expect to be given prior to chemotherapy?

   A. Ondansetron
   B. Allopurinol
   C. Dexamethasone
   D. Rasburicase

128. An 82-year-old woman with a history of breast cancer presents to the clinic with complaints of headaches for the past 2 weeks. She describes daily retro-orbital headaches that are worse in the morning. In addition, she notes severe nausea and vomiting. MRI of the brain reveals multiple metastatic lesions. Which of the following is the most appropriate initial management for this patient?

   A. Biopsy the lesions
   B. Surgical resection
   C. Dexamethasone
   D. Repeat MRI in 6 months

129. A 42-year-old man with a medical history significant for lung cancer is brought to an emergency room for altered mental status. His family reports that he altered his mental status for 3 days. He has been sluggish and difficult to arouse. On examination, he has orthostatic blood pressure and dry mucous membranes. Laboratory evaluation reveals Ca 14.5 mg/dl and Cr 2.0 mg/dl. Which of the following is the most appropriate initial management for this patient?

    A. 0.9% saline bolus
    B. Furosemide
    C. Pamidronate
    D. 0.45% saline bolus

130. A 34-year-old woman who has leukemia presents to the emergency room with a mild fever for less than 36 hours. A week previously, she completed a course of chemotherapy through a Hickman catheter. She only complains of fever and body pain. On examination, she is pale and febrile (101° F). Laboratory evaluation reveals a leukocyte count of 780 with 25% polymorphonuclear cells. Which of the following is the most appropriate therapy?

    A. Vancomycin, piperacillin-tazobactam, and gentamicin
    B. Amphotericin
    C. Both A and B
    D. None of these

131. A 71-year-old man who has lung cancer was admitted to the hospital with worsening dyspnea. He has complained of progressive dyspnea for a few months. What is the most likely diagnosis?

    A. Pericardial tamponade
    B. Congestive heart failure
    C. Superior vena cava (SVC) syndrome
    D. None of these

132.   Which of the following is a key component of the scope and standards of practice for oncology nursing?

   A. Collaborating with the interdisciplinary healthcare team.
   B. Providing palliative care for patients.
   C. Conducting research studies on new treatment modalities.
   D. Administering chemotherapy and radiation therapy.

133.   A 25-year-old man was recently diagnosed with leukemia. He is admitted to the hospital for further evaluation and chemotherapy initiation. He only complains of fatigue and malaise. Laboratory evaluation reveals pancytopenia, hyperkalemia (K 6.8), uric acid 13, hyperphosphatemia (12), and elevated lactate dehydrogenase (LDH). What is the most likely cause of his electrolyte abnormalities?

   A. Laboratory error
   B. Tumor lysis syndrome
   C. Hypercalcemia
   D. Acute renal failure

134.   Mr. Anderson, a 50-year-old patient with lung cancer, is receiving chemotherapy as an outpatient at an oncology clinic. He expresses concern to the nurse about a medication error that occurred during his previous visit. What should the nurse do first?

   A. Apologize to Mr. Anderson for the error and assure him that it won't happen again.
   B. Record Mr. Anderson's complaint in the incident report and inform the nurse manager.
   C. Encourage Mr. Anderson to report the error to the hospital's administration.
   D. Listen to Mr. Anderson's concerns, validate his feelings, and investigate the medication error.

135.   Which cell type is responsible for the production of antibodies in the immune system?

   A. T cells

B. Natural Killer cells

C. B cells

D. Macrophages

136. The HER2 gene amplification is associated with which type of cancer?

A. Breast cancer

B. Colorectal cancer

C. Lung cancer

D. Ovarian cancer

137. Sarah is an oncology nurse working in a radiation oncology department. What safety precautions should Sarah take to protect both herself and the patient during external beam radiation therapy?

A. Wearing gloves and a surgical mask.

B. Ensuring proper ventilation in the treatment room.

C. Using lead shielding devices for both the patient and herself.

D. Adhering to hand hygiene practices before and after patient contact.

138. Extravasation is a potential complication during chemotherapy administration. Which of the following interventions is not recommended for managing extravasations?

A. Applying cold compresses.

B. Administering antidotes or specific neutralizing agents.

C. Elevating the affected limb.

D. Administering chemotherapy into the same site.

139. Mr. Hernandez, a 40-year-old man, was diagnosed with terminal cancer six months ago. He has been receiving end-of-life care at home. Lately, his spouse has noticed that he often talks about not having enough time to complete his goals and regrets the things he will miss out on. Which nursing action would be most appropriate to help Mr. Hernandez cope with his anticipatory grief?

A. Encourage Mr. Hernandez to distract himself from negative thoughts.

B. Provide emotional support to Mr. Hernandez and his spouse.

C. Suggest Mr. Hernandez withdraw from all social activities.

D. Advise Mr. Hernandez to focus on planning for his spouse's future.

140. John, a 68-year-old male patient, has been diagnosed with lung cancer. Upon further evaluation, it is determined that the cancer has spread to the lymph nodes near the lungs. What is the most appropriate classification of John's lung cancer?

A. Stage I
B. Stage II
C. Stage III
D. Stage IV

141. Which of the following is a recommended intervention for managing diarrhea in patients with advanced colorectal cancer?

A. Increasing fiber intake.
B. Limiting fluid intake.
C. Administering antidiarrheal medications.
D. Encouraging frequent small meals.

142. Which of the following statements accurately reflects the financial concerns of cancer patients and their families?

A. Cancer treatment costs are typically fully covered by insurance, eliminating financial burden.
B. Cancer patients do not face any financial challenges because of available government support.
C. Cancer patients and their families often experience financial strain due to treatment-related expenses.
D. Cancer treatment costs are usually lower compared to other medical conditions.

143. Which nursing action is an example of patient advocacy in oncology practice?

A. Discussing treatment options with the patient and involving them in the decision-making process.

B. Administering chemotherapy without informing the patient about its potential side effects.

C. Withholding information about a patient's prognosis to prevent emotional distress.

D. Ignoring patient concerns and focusing solely on medical interventions.

144. Mr. Johnson, a 67-year-old male, is admitted to the oncology unit after undergoing surgery for pancreatic cancer. His laboratory reports show hyponatremia, decreased urine output, and increased urine osmolality. The oncologist suspects Syndrome of Inappropriate Antidiuretic Hormone Secretion (SIADH). Which of the following assessments should the nurse prioritize?

A. Monitoring intake and output measurements.

B. Assessing for signs of peripheral edema.

C. Measuring serum potassium levels.

D. Checking blood pressure every 4 hours.

145. Mrs. Anderson, a 55-year-old patient with breast cancer, completed her adjuvant chemotherapy three months ago. She recently noticed that her fingertips are becoming numb and tingly. Upon examination, her nurse practitioner suspects a delayed-onset side effect of chemotherapy. Which drug class could have caused this condition?

A. Alkylating agents

B. Antimetabolites

C. Taxanes

D. Platinum compounds

146. David is a 55-year-old patient receiving palliative care for stage IV lung cancer. The nurse is developing a care plan for David to address his specific needs. Which nursing intervention demonstrates adherence to standards of care in the nursing process for David's situation?

A. Administering pain medication as needed to alleviate discomfort.

B. Assisting David with daily activities of living, such as bathing and grooming.

C. Teaching David's family about the importance of advance care planning.

D. Collaborating with the interdisciplinary team to develop a holistic care plan.

147. Mark is a lung cancer survivor who is experiencing discrimination from his health insurance provider. He is denied coverage for a follow-up scan because of his previous cancer diagnosis. What should Mark do to address this discrimination concern?

    A. Accept the denial and forgo the follow-up scan.
    B. Discuss the issue with his healthcare provider.
    C. File a complaint with the employer who provides the health insurance.
    D. Seek legal advice to take legal action against the health insurance provider.

148. Ms. Johnson, a 55-year-old patient diagnosed with terminal lung cancer, has been experiencing profound grief since her diagnosis. She often expresses feelings of sadness, hopelessness, and a loss of purpose in life. As her oncology nurse, you understand the importance of addressing her psychosocial distress. Which of the following interventions would be most appropriate for Ms. Johnson?

    A. Encouraging her to suppress her emotions to facilitate acceptance of her diagnosis.
    B. Providing her with resources and information about support groups and counseling services.
    C. Advising her to keep her feelings to herself to prevent burdening her family.
    D. Suggesting distracting activities to divert her attention from grief and loss.

149. John, a 68-year-old patient, is receiving radiation therapy for prostate cancer. What is an important treatment-related consideration for him?

    A. Maintaining a low-fiber diet.
    B. Administering antiemetic medications.
    C. Monitoring for thrombocytopenia.
    D. Encouraging physical activity.

150. Which of the following is an appropriate intervention to support the caregiver of a patient receiving end-of-life care?

    A. Providing information on community resources and support groups
    B. Encouraging the caregiver to take regular breaks from caregiving responsibilities
    C. Teaching the caregiver relaxation techniques and stress management strategies
    D. All of the above

151. Which of the following is a characteristic feature of Syndrome of inappropriate antidiuretic hormone secretion (SIADH)?

    A. Hypernatremia
    B. Hypotonic urine
    C. Increased urine output
    D. Hypokalemia

152. John, a 50-year-old patient with leukemia, is currently undergoing chemotherapy. He develops a fever, chills, and fatigue after his most recent chemotherapy session. Upon assessment, the nurse finds that John has lower-than-normal white blood cell count. Which of the following is the most appropriate intervention for John?

    A. Administering a broad-spectrum antibiotic.
    B. Early ambulation to prevent pulmonary complications.
    C. Initiation of antiviral medication.
    D. Requesting a blood transfusion to increase white blood cell count.

153. What is the primary goal of navigation and coordination of care for oncology patients along the care continuum?

    A. Maximizing healthcare costs.
    B. Managing side effects of treatment.
    C. Minimizing patient interaction with healthcare providers.
    D. Improving patient outcomes and experiences.

154. Which patient is most likely to have a maladaptive response to a cancer diagnosis? A patient who reports:

    A. Feeling abandoned by God.
    B. Focusing on living in the present moment.
    C. Fighting the disease for his children.
    D. Praying and attending daily worship services.

155. What is the reason for foreign-born women with breast cancer having lower survival rates compared to women born in the United States?

    A. Histologic grade of the tumor.
    B. Access to mammography screening.
    C. The country from where the women have immigrated.
    D. Differences in the treatment protocols.

156. Which of the following patients with cancer is most likely to experience sexual dysfunction?

    A. A young patient who is newly married.
    B. A patient and partner who schedule time for sexual activity.
    C. A female patient with hypotension.
    D. A patient with a history of marital discord.

157. Which of the following is a common and preventable cause of anxiety for a patient with cancer?

    A. Uncontrolled pain
    B. Distressing memories
    C. Spiritual distress
    D. Sleep disburances

158. Social learning theory is characterized by which of the following actions?

    A. Collaborating to solve problems
    B. Setting personal goals
    C. Creating mnemonics

D. Imitating other's activities

159. Coping skills that rely on intrapsychic processes are referred to as:

    A. Avoidance-Focused.
    B. Appraisal-Focused.
    C. Emotion-Focused.
    D. Problem-Focused.

160. When should a premenopausal patient with cancer expect to resume menstruation following the completion of active treatment?

    A. 6 months
    B. 3 months
    C. 1 year
    D. 2 years

161. A patient's sister has tested positive for a BRCA mutation, but the patient has a negative result. The patient begins to cry and says, "I was always the bad child." What is the patient most likely experiencing?

    A. Reactive depression
    B. Sibling rivalry
    C. Survivor guilt
    D. Transmitter guilt

162. Which of the following offers the most likely reason that a patient with stage III cervical cancer may defer discussions about body image alterations and sexual intimacy prior to initiating treatment?

    A. Expectation of experiencing minimal symptoms of treatment.
    B. Unrealistic expectation of outcomes.
    C. Depersonalization of the disease experience.
    D. Concern of being perceived as vain.

163.   What is the correct term for the state of having lost a significant other?

    A. Bereavement
    B. Sadness
    C. Loss
    D. Grief

164.   A patient with extensive metastatic disease says, "I do not want any more therapy. I know I am going to die. I just want to go home." Which of the following is the nurse's best response?

    A. "Would you like to discuss hospice services?"
    B. "Have you discussed this at your support group?"
    C. "It is important that you continue with therapy."
    D. "I am sure you will feel better tomorrow."

165.   Which statement expressed by the spouse of a patient receiving services through the Hospice Medicare Benefit indicates an adequate understanding of the teaching provided?

    A. "I can expect a home health aide to come in several times a day to help me with meal preparation."
    B. "I should contact my hospice provider prior to taking my spouse to the emergency department."
    C. "Coverage for curative chemotherapy treatments will continue for the next several months."
    D. "This benefit will only cover medications deemed necessary to control my spouse's pain."

166.   Which intervention is most likely to assist a patient with cancer experiencing erectile dysfunction?

    A. Herbal dietary supplements
    B. Kegel exercises
    C. Psychotherapy
    D. Oral phosphodiesterase type 5 inhibitors

167. The nurse understands that anticipatory grief is:

    A. Unacknowledged.
    B. Long-Term.
    C. Unresolved.
    D. An Unconscious Process.

168. Which of the following behaviors demonstrated by the spouse of a patient who has died best exemplifies complicated grief?

    A. Removing all pictures from the house and refusing to discuss the decedent.
    B. Experiencing intermittent bouts of joy mixed with sorrow.
    C. Seeking out new organizations to join.
    D. Attending a support group for family members of cancer patients.

169. A patient with head and neck cancer who has completed treatment is at risk for which secondary malignancy?

    A. Lung cancer
    B. Glioblastoma
    C. Gastric cancer
    D. Breast cance

170. Prior to a fourth dose of cisplatin, a patient reports difficulty manipulating a toothbrush and silverware. The nurse's initial intervention is to:

    A. Instruct the patient to seek assistance with meals and oral hygiene.
    B. Arrange for an occupational therapy consultation.
    C. Reassure the patient that these problems are temporary side effects of the chemotherapy.
    D. Document the findings and report them to the physician.

171. A patient receiving docetaxel asks why dexamethasone is prescribed. The nurse's best response is that it prevents:

    A. Seizures.

B. Fatigue.
C. Anorexia.
D. Fluid retention.

172. Which of the folllowing offers the best explanation as to why a patient with metastatic breast cancer would experience pain at the site of metastasis with the initiation of tamoxifen? The patient is experiencing:

A. A common, temporary reaction to initial tamoxifen therapy.
B. An awkward sleeping position.
C. Further progression of the disease.
D. A psychosomatic reaction to the diagnosis of metastasis.

173. Which of the following is NOT a common symptom of cardiac tamponade in patients with cancer?

A. Dyspnea
B. Hypotension
C. Bradycardia
D. Jugular venous distention

Answer Key

Chapter Eight: Practice Test 1 | 137

Q.	1	2	3	4	5	6	7	8	9	10	11	12	13	14
A.	A	D	D	A	C	D	A	A	B	D	C	D	A	B

Q.	15	16	17	18	19	20	21	22	23	24	25	26	27	28
A.	D	A	A	D	C	C	D	A	C	A	D	B	A	C

Q.	29	30	31	32	33	34	35	36	37	38	39	40	41	42
A.	D	D	A	A	A	B	D	A	B	A	C	A	A	C

Q.	43	44	45	46	47	48	49	50	51	52	53	54	55	56
A.	C	C	C	B	C	C	A	C	D	A	C	B	C	B

Q.	57	58	59	60	61	62	63	64	65	66	67	68	69	70
A.	C	B	A	A	D	B	D	C	A	D	A	C	A	A

Q.	71	72	73	74	75	76	77	78	79	80	81	82	83	84
A.	D	D	B	B	A	A	D	A	B	B	D	A	C	C

Q.	85	86	87	88	89	90	91	92	93	94	95	96	97	98
A.	A	A	C	B	D	C	C	D	A	B	B	D	C	C

Q.	99	100	101	102	103	104	105	106	107	108	109	110	111	112
A.	A	A	A	A	C	A	B	B	A	B	C	C	C	B

Q.	113	114	115	116	117	118	119	120	121	122	123	124	125	126
A.	A	C	A	C	D	D	A	C	D	C	C	B	A	B

Q.	127	128	129	130	131	132	133	134	135	136	137	138	139	140
A.	D	C	A	A	C	A	B	D	C	A	C	D	B	C

Q.	141	142	143	144	145	146	147	148	149	150	151	152	153	154
A.	C	C	A	A	C	D	D	B	C	D	B	A	D	A

Q.	155	156	157	158	159	160	161	162	163	164	165	166	167	168
A.	B	D	A	D	C	B	C	D	A	A	B	D	D	A

Q.	169	170	171	172	173
A.	A	D	D	A	C

Answers and Explanations

1.   A: Implanted ports have a lower risk of infection than tunneled central venous catheters.

2.   D: Living wills are designed to determine the care that a patient is agreeable to receive or not receive in the event of a terminal illness.

3.   D: Hair loss from chemotherapy usually begins two weeks after beginning treatment.

4.   A: The risk of secondary leukemia increases with the use of alkylating agents.

5.   C: By being aware of their bowel habits, a patient will be able to better plan sexual activities around expected bowel movements.

6.   D: A patient with ovarian cancer is at risk for the development of a secondary melanoma of the eye.

7.   A: Follow-up telephone calls are known to help with medication adherence.

8.   A: Having a mother who was diagnosed with breast cancer before the age of 60 years has an associated relative risk of 2 to 4 times of those without this risk factor.

9.   B: A survivorship care plan is provided to a patient upon the completion of treatment to provide information on the treatments received, possible long term effects, and healthy lifestyle choices and screenings throughout a patient's lifetime.

10.   D: Primary prevention refers to measures for the prevention of the disease such as immunization, avoiding tobacco or reducing exposure to ultraviolet rays.

11.   C: Patients with Hodgkin lymphoma have an increased risk of secondary malignacy including leukemia and myelodysplastic syndrome, non-Hodgkin lymphoma, breast, lung and thyroid.

12.   D: Chemotherapy, especially with cisplatin and alkylating agents can cause permanent infertility (azoospermia). Sperm banking is recommended prior to the start of treatment if the patient is interested in future paternity.

13.   A: Repetition of concepts and using multiple ways to convey a message is recommended, including the use of pictures and demonstrations.

14.   B: When therapies such as IV opioids, oxygen, diuretics, and benzodiazepines fail to improve intractable dyspnea, palliative sedation is considered in end-of-life care.

15.   D: Teaching about risk factors and the importance of testicular self-examination beginning in the teen years is the most important prevention method.

16.   A: Individuals at particular risk for undertreatment of pain symptoms at the end of life are the elderly, minorities, and women.

17.   A: The possibility of reduced work schedules, and support from coworkers are factors that can facilitate a smoother transition into the workforce following treatment.

18.   D: The extent of nutrition intervention depends on the cause of weight loss and overall goals of the patient and healthcare team.

19.   C: Neglecting the quality of life can lead to premature death either by suicide or passive surrender.

20.   C: Cultural competence suggests that healthcare professionals demonstrate the ability to recognize the cultural differences in society and respect those differences in the treatment of all patients that they encounter.

21.   D: The American Cancer Society recommends a shared-decision making conversation about prostate-specific antigen testing and digital rectal examination beginning at age 45 for men with a high risk of developing prostate cancer.

22.   A: Patient teaching after receiving chemotherapy includes follow-up care and symptom management. The risks and symptoms of infection are most important.

23.   C: The combined use of alcohol and tobacco synergistically increases the risk of laryngeal cancer by about 50%.

24.   A: Oral contraceptives are recommended to aid in prevention of ovarian cancer families with Lynch syndrome, not genetically at risk for breast cancer.

25.   D: Lenalidomide is only available under the REVAssist® program to ensure patients are properly informed of fetal risks.

26.   B: Advance directives are based on the principle of autonomy.

27.   A: It is recommended that the patient avoid inserting anything into the vagina for four weeks following a loop electrosurgical excision procedure.

28.   C: It is estimated that 80% of colon cancers can be prevented by dietary change.

29.   D: Palmar-plantar erythrodysesthesia changes to skin can be related to capillary rupture occurring while walking or during other weight-bearing activities.

30.   D: When treatment fails, the nurse should explore the patient's feelings about hearing the news rather than focusing on the treatment possibilities discussed with the physician.

31.   A: Lymphedema rates are 0% to 5% for women after a sentinel lymph node procedure and 10%-30% after axillary lymph node dissection.

32. A: Self-breast exams should be performed 7 to 10 days after the start of menses (the patient's period...this is the first day of bleeding). Breast tissue is soft at this time due to hormone levels.

33. A: The best time to perform a self-testicular exam is after a shower when the scrotum is descended and the tissue is soft. This makes it easier to feel lumps or masses.

34. B: Sealed radiation therapy patients are radioactive for 4-8 hours. Staff should be rotated out and never required to provide care for more than one patient at a time. This decreases radiation exposure.

35. D: Patients who have undergone a bone marrow transplant are at major risk for bleeding and infection. The bone marrow is responsible for producing infection and bleeding-fighting agents such as WBCs and platelets. Therefore, when a patient receives this from a donor, it takes time for the body to build up normal levels.

36. A: During this period, bone marrow suppression is the greatest; therefore, the platelet count may be extremely low.

37. B: Clinically, the patient will present with the following: decreased hgb and hct, decreased platelets, and elevated or normal WBCs with enlarged lymph nodes. This is because leukemia affects the bone marrow. The bone marrow is a vital organ that is responsible for producing platelets, white blood cells, and red blood cells.

38. A: This is a hallmark of Multiple myeloma.

39. C: Multiple myeloma is proliferation of plasma cells. This causes increased uric acid and calcium levels. This, therefore, increases the patient's risk for renal failure and bone problems. Encourage fluids to keep the kidneys "flushed" and skeletal support for the bones helps with further complications.

40.   A: Due to the patient's young age of a first sexual encounter (any age before 17 is significant) and multiple sex partners, drastically increases a person risk of cervical cancer.

41.   A: All options are incorrect except for "Masses are usually felt in the upper outer quadrant beneath the nipple or axilla."

42.   C: Regular exercise and physical activity have been shown to decrease stress levels and improve overall mental well-being. Engaging in physical activity can help Emma to alleviate the symptoms of compassion fatigue, as it promotes the release of endorphins, which are known as "feel-good" hormones.

43.   C: Culturally congruent care in oncology nursing practice entails recognizing and respecting patients' cultural beliefs, values, traditions, and preferences. It involves tailoring care to meet their unique cultural needs, ensuring that interventions are aligned with their cultural values and practices. By providing culturally congruent care, nurses can enhance patient satisfaction, trust, and compliance, which can ultimately improve health outcomes.

44.   C: As an oncology certified nurse, collaboration with the healthcare team is crucial in the navigation and coordination of care for patients like Mrs. Johnson. By actively participating in developing a comprehensive care plan, the nurse ensures that all aspects of care are considered, including symptom management, medication administration, and patient education.

45.   C: Hormone therapy is a targeted therapy used in the treatment of hormone receptor-positive cancers, such as breast cancer or prostate cancer. It works by either blocking the production of hormones or preventing the hormones from binding to cancer cells, thereby inhibiting their growth.

46.   B: Respecting patient autonomy is an essential aspect of patient advocacy and ethical practice. Sarah has the right to be informed about her condition and make decisions regarding her treatment. The nurse should provide all the necessary information to Sarah, enabling her to understand the implications of different treatment options. By respecting her autonomy, the nurse empowers Sarah to make an informed decision that aligns with her values and goals of care.

47.   C: When it comes to the approval of insurance claims for cancer treatment, several factors may come into play. The type of cancer may not directly affect claim approval since insurance coverage is generally based on the type of treatment required rather than the specific cancer diagnosis. The age of the patient and employment status may have indirect implications for insurance coverage. However, pre-existing medical conditions can significantly impact the approval of insurance claims as insurance providers may consider them when determining coverage eligibility and may impose waiting periods or exclusions for pre-existing conditions.

48.   C: Encouraging relaxation techniques and deep breathing exercises. Dyspnea in patients with advanced lung cancer can be relieved by non-pharmacological approaches, and relaxation techniques like guided imagery and deep breathing exercises can help decrease anxiety and dyspnea.

49.   A: Neutropenia, a decrease in the number of neutrophils, is a common side effect of cancer treatment, especially chemotherapy and radiation therapy. These therapies can suppress bone marrow function, leading to a decrease in neutrophil production. Neutrophils play a crucial role in the body's defense against infections, and their decreased level increases the risk of developing serious and potentially life-threatening infections.

50.   C: The nurse should conduct a literature review to gather evidence on the effectiveness of ginger and acupuncture in managing chemotherapy-induced nausea and vomiting.

51. D: The presence of bilateral lower-extremity weakness and changes in bowel and bladder function indicate significant spinal cord compression. The most appropriate intervention in this scenario is to initiate immediate radiation therapy to relieve the compression and prevent further neurological damage.

52. A: Chronic inflammation plays a pivotal role in the development of cervical cancer. Persistent infection with high-risk strains of human papillomavirus (HPV), which is transmitted sexually, leads to chronic inflammation of the cervix. This chronic inflammation promotes the transformation of normal cervical cells into precancerous and eventually cancerous cells.

53. C: Blood and marrow transplant can be performed using the patient's own healthy cells through an autologous transplant or cells from a donor through an allogeneic transplant.

54. B: When a patient has impaired mobility due to musculoskeletal alterations, it is important to promote joint flexibility and prevent further decline in functioning.

55. C: Encouraging Emily to journal her thoughts and feelings can help her explore and express her spiritual distress. Writing can be a therapeutic tool, allowing individuals to reflect on their emotions and gain insight into their own thoughts.

56. B: The scenario depicts signs of bowel obstruction, which is a critical oncologic emergency. Surgical intervention is necessary to relieve the obstruction and restore bowel function.

57. C: Implementing relaxation techniques, such as deep breathing exercises, meditation, and guided imagery, can help reduce stress levels and promote better sleep, ultimately aiding in the management of fatigue.

58.   B: The femur is frequently affected as it is the largest and strongest bone in the body, rich in blood supply, making it an ideal site for metastasis from breast cancer cells. Additionally, the bone marrow within the femur provides a suitable environment for cancer cells to grow and create secondary tumors.

59.   A: The role of the oncology certified nurse in end-of-life care is to collaborate with the interdisciplinary team, including the patient, family, and other healthcare providers, to develop a comprehensive care plan.

60.   A: Chemotherapy will decrease the response by the immune system by causing neutropenia, anemia, and thrombocytopenia, collectively known as Myelosuppression.

61.   D: Alkalyting agents break the DNA helix strand and interfere with DNA replication.

62.   B: A plastic face shield should be used when splashing of hazardous drugs is possible. Intravesical administration carries a risk of splashing.

63.   D: The goal of adjuvant therapy is to target minimal, residual disease for patients at high risk of developing metastasis.

64.   C: Hormone therapy has been successfully used to treat breast and prostate cancers.

65.   A: Patients are to be instructed to take temozolomide on an empty stomach at bedtime to decrease the risk of nausea and vomiting.

66.   D: Vincristine is fatal if administered intrathecally.

67.   A: Chronic myeloid leukemia is most likely to be treated by an allogeneic transplant.

68.   C: Nadir varies but typically occurs 7-10 days after chemotherapy.

69. A: Administration of high-dose chemotherapy helps eliminate residual disease prior to a hematopoietic stem cell transplant.

70. A: Life-threatening adverse reactions to posaconazole can include Torsades de Pointes, hepatocellular damage, and allergic reactions.

71. D: Surgery is a cancer treatment modality that can be used along with chemotherapy radiation or may be used alone and can be the only treatment that a patient will require.

72. D: Tacrolimus is an immunosuppressant used to prevent organ rejection.

73. B: Chemotherapy started after the first trimester has fewer complications and poses less risk to the fetus.

74. B: A colon cancer with staging T2 N2 M1 is a stage IV cancer, which is advanced metastatic cancer. The cure is not possible with unresectable disease. Chemotherapy in this setting is given until the disease progresses.

75. A: Allogeneic stem cell transplant types may be either myeloablative or nonmyeloablative and can be used to treat acute lymphocytic leukemia, among other malignant and nonmalignant blood disorders.

76. A: Radiotherapy for muscle-invasive bladder cancer can be used to preserve the bladder and maximize quality of life without compromising long-term disease-specific survival.

77. D: Fluorouracil increases the risk of mucositis either alone or in combination with other chemotherapy agents.

78. A: The risk of pneumonitis is increased when having a large volume of lung included in the treatment field.

79. B: Asparaginase is used IV, SC, or IM for patients diagnosed with acute lymphocytic leukemia.

80. B: It is imperative that patients who are sexually active and fertile use a reliable form of birth control.

81.   D: Patients receiving oxaliplatin should be instructed to avoid ice and cold foods and fluids during the infusion.

82.   A: Nursing care management of the patient receiving intraperitoneal drug administration includes encouraging repositioning from side to side every 15 minutes during the dwell time.

83.   C: Protein kinase inhibitors are small molecules that work by blocking the binding site on the intracellular portion of a receptor.

84.   C: Chimeric antibodies are made up of approximately 70% human and 30% foreign antibodies.

85.   A: Adjuvant radiation therapy in early-stage breast cancer involves providing radiation therapy after surgery to destroy gross or microscopic residual disease with the goal of preventing tumor recurrence.

86.   A: Alcohol irritates the mucosa and may delay healing.

87.   C: Pretreatment guidelines for methotrexate include hydration to prevent renal injury.

88.   B: Monoclonal antibodies bind to the tumor cell and prevent ligand-receptor binding by blocking other molecules from attaching to the cell, thus preventing the rapid growth of cancer cells.

89.   D: Etoposide is a known human carcinogen.

90.   C: In this scenario, Jane's alterations in functioning are manifested as difficulty in performing ADLs due to weakness and fatigue. Suggesting adaptive equipment, such as assistive devices or modifications to the environment, can help improve her independence and reduce the physical strain associated with ADLs. It is essential to preserve Jane's autonomy and minimize caregiver burden.

91.   C: Graft-versus-host disease (GVHD) is a common complication associated with blood and marrow transplant (BMT)..

92.   D: Transcutaneous electrical nerve stimulation (TENS) is a non-pharmacological intervention that helps in managing pain for cancer patients.

93.   A: The most appropriate nursing intervention for managing dry and itchy skin, a common side effect of targeted therapy Erlotinib, is to apply a high-potency topical corticosteroid.

94.   B: Hormone therapy is often employed in breast cancer patients to block the production or reduce the effects of estrogen in the body. However, a chronic side effect of long-term hormone therapy is the development of osteoporosis.

95.   B: Referring Mary to a financial counselor who can provide information on assistance programs is the most appropriate intervention for addressing her financial concerns.

96.   D: Elevating the head of the bed promotes venous drainage and helps reduce intracranial pressure in patients with brain metastasis. It is an essential intervention in managing increased intracranial pressure, which can help alleviate the symptoms and prevent further complications.

97.   C: Understanding cultural, spiritual, and religious beliefs can enhance patient-centered care.

98.   C: Facilitating peer interaction and emotional support.

99.   A: "I should try to push myself to do more even if I feel tired."

100. A: "Molecular testing helps to identify genetic mutations that increase the risk of developing certain types of cancer."

101. A: The Americans with Disabilities Act (ADA) prohibits discrimination against individuals with disabilities, which includes cancer survivors. The ADA defines disability as a physical or mental impairment that substantially limits one or more major life activities. Cancer survivors may face discrimination in the workplace, but they are protected by the ADA.

102. A: Assisting the individual in exploring personal values and beliefs.

103.   C: Environmental factors play a significant role in the process of carcinogenesis.. Oncology nurses play a vital role in educating patients about these factors and supporting them in making lifestyle modifications to reduce their risk.

104.   A: Epidemiology in oncology aims to identify and manage risk factors associated with cancer development.

105.   B: The presence of petechiae and ecchymosis along with a low platelet count indicates increased risk of bleeding. Administering a platelet transfusion would help increase the patient's platelet count and reduce the risk of bleeding complications.

106.   B: Acupuncture is a complementary modality that involves the insertion of thin needles into specific points on the body.

107.   A: Changes in breast appearance or shape can be an early indicator of breast cancer recurrence. It is important for Sarah to be aware of any new lumps, dimpling, redness, or swelling on or around her breast.

108.   B: Disclosing medical conditions like cancer during a job interview is not necessary unless it is mandated by law or if it directly impacts the individual's ability to perform the essential functions of the job.

109.   C: Assisting Michael and his spouse in exploring other non-sexual ways to foster intimacy and emotional connection.

110.   C: Cancer rehabilitation is not solely focused on managing pain and discomfort but encompasses a multidisciplinary approach to address the physical, emotional, cognitive, and social aspects of cancer survivors' lives.

111.   C: Penile rehabilitation involves the use of medications to treat post-prostatectomy erectile dysfunction. It is an integral part of prostate cancer survivorship care, specifically addressing the restoration of erectile function post-prostatectomy.

112. B: Music therapy is a non-pharmacologic comfort measure that can significantly contribute to emotional support for patients receiving end-of-life care. It involves the use of music and sound to enhance the patient's emotional well-being, promote relaxation, reduce anxiety, and facilitate self-expression. Music has the power to evoke memories, provide comfort, and create a peaceful environment.

113. A: Providing reassurance and empathy is a therapeutic communication technique that helps foster trust, understanding, and a positive relationship between the nurse and the oncology patient.

114. C: Non-modifiable risk factors are those that cannot be changed or controlled. In this scenario, Mrs. Johnson's family history of breast cancer is a non-modifiable risk factor that increases her own risk of developing the disease. Studies have shown that having a first-degree relative (such as a mother) with breast cancer can approximately double a woman's risk.

115. A: Mr. Anderson's age increases his risk of colorectal cancer.

116. C: Mr. Anderson's genetic factors can modify his risk of colorectal cancer.

117. D: Collaborate with a social worker to explore financial assistance programs and resources available to Mr. Johnson.

118. D: Acknowledging and respecting the unique cultural perspectives and values of the patient.

119. A: Assess Mrs. Johnson's pain and consult with the healthcare provider for a potential change in pain medication.

120. C: The most appropriate nursing intervention in this scenario is to discontinue the infusion immediately. The symptoms described indicate a hypersensitivity reaction, which can progress to anaphylaxis. Discontinuing the infusion is crucial to prevent further exposure to the triggering agent.

121.   D: When a patient develops radiation-induced dermatitis, it is important to prioritize interventions that promote skin integrity and minimize further damage. Using mild soap and patting the skin dry gently helps maintain cleanliness without causing excessive friction or trauma to the affected area.

122.   C: Pre-existing medical conditions can significantly impact the approval of insurance claims as insurance providers may consider them when determining coverage eligibility and may impose waiting periods or exclusions for pre-existing conditions.

123.   C: Encouraging relaxation techniques and deep breathing exercises. Dyspnea in patients with advanced lung cancer can be relieved by non-pharmacological approaches, and relaxation techniques like guided imagery and deep breathing exercises can help decrease anxiety and dyspnea.

124.   B: The priority nursing action in this scenario is to ensure the patient's airway is open and provide oxygen support. These symptoms are indicative of anaphylaxis, a severe, life-threatening allergic reaction. Maintaining a patent airway and administering oxygen can help stabilize the patient's breathing and oxygenation.

125.   A: When patients experience a loss of personal control over their lives due to the diagnosis and treatment of cancer, it is crucial for healthcare professionals to promote patient autonomy and involvement in their care. Encouraging the patient to make decisions regarding their treatment gives them a sense of empowerment and allows them to maintain some control over their situation. Involving the patient in decision-making can enhance their psychological well-being and help them cope better with the challenges of their condition.

126.   B: Identify patients at risk and assess each interaction.

127.   D: Rasburicase. This is due to increased uric acid.

128. C: Dexamethasone is the appropriate initial treatment for this patient. Daily retro-orbital headaches, severe nausea, and vomiting suggest increased intracranial pressure. The MRI indicates multiple metastatic lesions in the brain due to breast cancer.

129. A: A 0.9% saline bolus should be given as the first treatment to correct dehydration and improve renal perfusion, which lowers serum calcium levels..

130. A: Vancomycin, piperacillin-tazobactam, and gentamicin are the recommended antibiotics for this patient presenting with fever and leukopenia, indicating neutropenic fever, a common complication of chemotherapy. This combination of antibiotics provides broad-spectrum coverage against both gram-positive and gram-negative bacteria.

131. C: Superior vena cava (SVC) syndrome.

132. A: The scope and standards of practice for oncology nursing emphasize the importance of collaboration with the interdisciplinary healthcare team.

133. B: Patient likely has tumor lysis syndrome, causing electrolyte abnormalities due to cancer cell release. Elevated LDH supports diagnosis. Symptoms consistent with condition.

134. D: Listen to Mr. Anderson's concerns, validate his feelings, and investigate the medication error.

135. C: B cells play a crucial role in the immune response by producing antibodies. Upon encountering an antigen, B cells undergo activation and differentiate into plasma cells, which are responsible for antibody production. These antibodies can neutralize pathogens and enhance the process of phagocytosis.

136. A: The HER2 (Human Epidermal growth factor Receptor 2) gene amplification is commonly identified in breast cancer patients.

137. C: Using lead shielding devices for both the patient and herself.

138.   D: Administering chemotherapy into the same site where extravasation has occurred is not recommended. It could further damage the surrounding tissues and potentially exacerbate the adverse effects.

139.   B: Anticipatory grief occurs when individuals experience the process of mourning before an actual loss occurs. In this scenario, The most appropriate nursing action is to provide emotional support to both Mr. Hernandez and his spouse, as it helps validate their feelings and concerns.

140.   C: Stage III lung cancer indicates that the cancer has spread beyond the lung to the nearby lymph nodes, but it has not yet metastasized to distant organs. It is characterized by the involvement of lymph nodes that are located on the same side as the primary tumor.

141.   C: Administering antidiarrheal medications.

142.   C: Financial concerns are a significant aspect of the psychosocial dimensions of care for cancer patients. Cancer treatment involves various expenses, such as hospital bills, medication costs, and additional supportive services. These expenses can create a significant financial burden for patients and their families.

143.   A: Discussing treatment options with the patient and involving them in the decision-making process.

144.   A: Monitoring intake and output measurements (A) is crucial in assessing fluid balance and detecting any further water retention in patients with SIADH. It helps determine the effectiveness of fluid restriction or other interventions.

145.   C: Taxanes, such as paclitaxel and docetaxel, are known to cause peripheral neuropathy, which manifests as numbness, tingling, or loss of sensation in the fingertips and toes. This delayed-onset side effect can occur several months after completion of chemotherapy.

146.   D: Adhering to standards of care in the nursing process for palliative care involves collaboration with the interdisciplinary team.

147. D: Discrimination in health insurance based on pre-existing conditions, such as a previous cancer diagnosis, is illegal. Mark should not accept the denial without seeking further action.

148. B: The most appropriate intervention for Ms. Johnson is to provide her with resources and information about support groups and counseling services.

149. C: Radiation therapy can cause a decrease in platelet count, leading to thrombocytopenia. Monitoring for thrombocytopenia is crucial to detect any abnormalities in platelet levels. This allows for timely intervention to prevent bleeding complications.

150. D: Providing comprehensive support to the caregiver is essential in end-of-life care. Option A is crucial as it enables the caregiver to access additional help and emotional support through community resources and support groups.

151. B: SIADH is a condition characterized by the excessive release of antidiuretic hormone (ADH), leading to water retention and impaired water excretion. One of the diagnostic criteria for SIADH is the presence of hypotonic urine, which means that the urine has a lower concentration of solutes compared to the plasma. This occurs due to the increased reabsorption of water in the kidneys under the influence of ADH.

152. A: The presence of fever, chills, and fatigue in a patient with low white blood cell count after chemotherapy indicates the risk of infection. In this case, the most appropriate intervention would be to administer a broad-spectrum antibiotic to prevent or treat any potential bacterial infections.

153. D: The primary goal of navigation and coordination of care for oncology patients along the care continuum is to improve patient outcomes and experiences.

154.   A: Negative religious coping, such as constantly pleading for God's intervention or passively deferring decisions to God, is strongly associated with maladaptive responses to illness.

155.   B: Patients from other countries may face significant barriers to receiving recommended screenings and care, leading to diagnosis at later stages and lower survival rates.

156.   D: Patients who have marital issues in their relationships before a diagnosis of cancer will be a greater risk for sexual difficulties.

157.   A: Chronic anxiety and depression can be caused by chronic, poorly controlled pain.

158.   D: Social learning theory indicates that learning takes place by watching and imitating others.

159.   C: Emotion-focused coping relies on the processes that elicit emotions, feeling, concerns.

160.   B: If premenopausal women do not experience a return of menses within 3 months of treatment completion, ovarian failure is considered to be permanent.

161.   C: Survivor guilt occurs when a person tests negative and feel guilty as to why they were fortunate enough to test negative when a relative tested positive.

162.   D: Patients often feel that they are being vain and may be embarrassed if they want to discuss sexuality in light of how serious their illness is.

163.   A: With the pronouncement of death, those who have the closest blood or legal connections to the deceased are considered the bereaved.

164. A: When treatment options have been exhausted, or when a patient decides that they wish to discontinue treatment, a hospice referral is a reasonable expectation. Patients can be afraid to ask for hospice care and nurses should stress that hospice is a philosophy of care rather than a facility that they would be sent to.

165. B: Patients and families should be taught to contact the contracted hospice provider prior to calling an ambulance for transport to an emergency department.

166. D: Literature depicts that an evidence-based practice intervention of treating erectile dysfunction with oral phosphodiesterase type 5 inhibitor medications have been recommended for practice.

167. D: Anticipatory grief is an unconscious process that can be brought on by receiving bad news.

168. A: Complicated grief is unresolved grief that persists over time and interferes with the ability to perform activities of daily living

169. A: A secondary malignancy affecting the skin and mucosa after treatment for head and neck cancer can be an oral/buccal cancer or lung cancer.

170. D: Cisplatin can cause neurotoxicity, particularly at cumulative doses of more than 300-500mg/m2. Numbness and pain will generally begin in the fingers and toes and continue proximally.

171. D: Docetaxel is associated with fluid retention and associated alveolar permeability and pulmonary infiltrates that may be prevented with corticosteroids premedication.

172. A: Initiation of tamoxifen can result in a tumor flare. This is transient and usually resolves even with continued therapy.

173. C: Bradycardia is not typically seen in patients with cardiac tamponade.

Chapter Nine: Practice Test 2

1.   Mr. Johnson, a 68-year-old male, is being evaluated for symptoms suggestive of prostate cancer. His prostate-specific antigen (PSA) level is elevated, and the physician now wants to perform a prostate biopsy. Which diagnostic measure is most appropriate for confirming prostate cancer?

   A. Transrectal ultrasound (TRUS)-guided biopsy
   B. Digital rectal examination (DRE)
   C. Prostate biopsy via open surgery
   D. Prostate magnetic resonance imaging (MRI)

2.   Which preventive health practice is recommended to reduce the risk of skin cancer?

   A. Regular use of sunscreen
   B. Regular consumption of red meat
   C. Limiting physical activity
   D. Maintaining a sedentary lifestyle

3.   Mr. Johnson, a 62-year-old patient with colorectal cancer, completed his radiation therapy six months ago. Lately, he has been experiencing progressive fatigue and shortness of breath upon mild exertion. His hemoglobin level is significantly decreased. Which delayed-onset side effect of radiation therapy is likely responsible for these symptoms?

   A. Radiation pneumonitis

    B. Radiation dermatitis

    C. Radiation enteritis

    D. Radiation-induced bone marrow suppression

4. Jonathan, a 60-year-old man, is undergoing chemotherapy for lung cancer. He feels frustrated and angry due to the loss of personal control over his daily activities and self- care. He expresses his dissatisfaction with having to rely on others for assistance. Which nursing intervention is most suitable to address Jonathan's feelings of loss of personal control?

    A. Collaborating with Jonathan to develop a schedule that allows him to be involved in his care

    B. Restricting visitors and activities to reduce stress and frustration

    C. Assigning a nursing assistant to meet all of Jonathan's needs promptly

    D. Encouraging Jonathan to suppress and ignore his negative emotions

5. Amelia, a 54-year-old patient with stage III non-small cell lung cancer, has been receiving immunotherapy as part of her treatment plan. Today, she presents to the oncology clinic with complaints of dyspnea, cough, and chest pain. On physical examination, she appears fatigued, and pulmonary auscultation reveals decreased breath sounds on the left side. A chest X-ray shows a large pleural effusion. Which of the following complications of immunotherapy is most likely responsible for Amelia's symptoms?

    A. Pneumonitis

    B. Myocarditis

    C. Nephritis

    D. Dermatitis

6. Sarah, a 45-year-old patient with advanced-stage cancer, is currently receiving palliative care at a hospice facility. Her sister, Emily, is the primary caregiver and is experiencing high levels of stress and burnout. Which strategy would be most effective in providing caregiver support to Emily?

    A. Providing education on self-care techniques and stress management.

    B. Encouraging Emily to focus more on Sarah's physical needs.

    C. Advising Emily to limit her visits to the hospice facility.

D. Suggesting Emily seek professional healthcare training.

7.   Mr. Johnson, a 55-year-old patient with metastatic lung cancer, presents to the emergency department with a sudden change in his neurologic status. He is disoriented, has slurred speech, and complains of a severe headache. The nurse suspects increased intracranial pressure (ICP) and checks Mr. Johnson's vital signs. Which vital sign finding is indicative of increased ICP?

A. Hypotension (low blood pressure)
B. Tachycardia (rapid heart rate)
C. Hypothermia (low body temperature)
D. Bradypnea (slow respiratory rate)

8.   Which of the following is a key aspect of the scientific basis of oncology nursing practice?

A. Providing spiritual support to cancer patients and their families.
B. Administering chemotherapy drugs to patients.
C. Conducting research studies to investigate new cancer treatments.
D. Collaborating with social workers to address psychosocial needs of patients.

9.   Mr. Davis, a 65-year-old patient with advanced lung cancer, is admitted to the oncology unit complaining of persistent cough and shortness of breath. These symptoms have been present for several months and have worsened recently. The nurse suspects that Mr. Davis is experiencing chronic lung cancer-associated symptoms. Which of the following options provides an accurate explanation for the etiology and pattern of symptoms associated with chronic lung cancer?

A. Chronic lung cancer-associated symptoms occur when cigarette smoke triggers long-term inflammation in the lungs, leading to a persistent cough, dyspnea, wheezing, and clubbing of the fingers.
B. Chronic lung cancer-associated symptoms are caused by the gradual proliferation of cancer cells in the lung tissue, resulting in a persistent cough, hoarseness, stridor, and pleural effusion.
C. Chronic lung cancer-associated symptoms are characterized by the

spread of cancer cells from the lung to other distant sites, causing fatigue, weight loss, anemia, and lymphedema.

D. Chronic lung cancer-associated symptoms occur due to chronic exposure to asbestos, leading to cough, dyspnea, chest pain, and thrombocytopenia.

10. Which coping mechanism involves the individual seeking support and comfort from others in times of distress?

   A. Rationalization
   B. Denial
   C. Social support
   D. Intellectualization

11. Which dietary modification is most appropriate for a patient experiencing xerostomia as a result of chemotherapy?

   A. Increasing intake of citrus fruits
   B. Reducing fluid intake
   C. Avoiding spicy and acidic foods
   D. Consuming a high-protein diet

12. Which of the following is not a type of adaptive immune response?

   A. Humoral immunity
   B. Cellular immunity
   C. Innate immunity
   D. Delayed-type hypersensitivity

13. Which of the following is an important aspect to consider when conducting a clinical trial for oncology patients?

   A. Informed consent
   B. Random assignment of patients
   C. Placebo administration
   D. Single-blind study design

14. Mr. Johnson, a 58-year-old male, has been diagnosed with colorectal cancer. The tumor has invaded through the wall of the colon but has not spread to nearby lymph nodes or distant sites. The histological grade indicates a moderate differentiation of tumor cells. Which stage and histological grade best describe Mr. Johnson's cancer?

    A. Stage II, Grade 2
    B. Stage I, Grade 3
    C. Stage III, Grade 1
    D. Stage IV, Grade 4

15. Which complementary and integrative modality involves the application of pressure to specific points on the body to promote relaxation and alleviate pain?

    A. Massage therapy
    B. Acupuncture
    C. Herbal supplements
    D. Meditation

16. Which laboratory value should be closely monitored during chemotherapy administration?

    A. Platelet count
    B. Blood urea nitrogen (BUN) level
    C. Serum potassium level
    D. Total cholesterol level

17. Which of the following symptoms is NOT commonly associated with depression?

    A. Fatigue
    B. Insomnia
    C. Weight gain
    D. Feelings of guilt

18. Mrs. Sanchez, a 68-year-old female, has undergone a mastectomy for breast cancer. She is scheduled to receive adjuvant radiation therapy. The nurse is providing education to Mrs. Sanchez about the possible side effects of radiation. Which of the following statements by Mrs. Sanchez indicates a need for further clarification?

    A. "I may experience skin redness and irritation in the area being treated."
    B. "Radiation therapy may cause fatigue, but it should improve with time."
    C. "I will need to avoid sun exposure during radiation treatment."
    D. "Radiation therapy can increase the risk of infection."

19. John, a 60-year-old male with advanced lung cancer, is enrolled in a clinical trial evaluating the efficacy of a new combination therapy. Two weeks into the trial, he experiences severe adverse reactions to the experimental treatment. What should the nurse do first in this situation?

    A. Immediately inform the principal investigator about the adverse reactions.
    B. Stop the administration of the experimental treatment and assess John's condition.
    C. Document the adverse reactions and report them to the institutional review board.
    D. Inform John about the potential risks of participating in a clinical trial.

20. What is the primary role of an oncology nurse in patient advocacy?

    A. To prioritize the physician's recommendations over the patient's preferences.
    B. To ensure patients adhere to treatment plans through coercion if necessary.
    C. To protect patient confidentiality by withholding information from family members.
    D. To support and represent the best interests of patients during their cancer journey.

21. John, a gay man, is diagnosed with testicular cancer. He is scheduled for surgery to remove the affected testicle. As his oncology nurse, which action demonstrates providing culturally competent care?

    A. Assuring John that testicular cancer is not common among gay men.
    B. Avoiding any discussion about John's sexual orientation during his hospital stay.
    C. Asking John if he has a sexual partner and providing information about support services tailored for the LGBTQ+ community.
    D. Dismissing any concerns John may have about the impact of the cancer diagnosis on his sexual orientation.

22. Mr. Harris, a 65-year-old patient, completed treatment for colon cancer several years ago. He is concerned about the risk of developing subsequent malignancies after his initial diagnosis. The oncology nurse explains the concept of subsequent malignancies during a follow-up visit. Which of the following statements by the nurse is correct regarding subsequent malignancies?

    A. "The risk of subsequent malignancies decreases significantly after 5 years of cancer remission."
    B. "Subsequent malignancies are more likely to occur in the same organ or site as the initial cancer."
    C. "Patients with a family history of cancer are not at an increased risk of subsequent malignancies."
    D. "Surgery for the initial cancer increases the risk of developing subsequent malignancies."

23. Which coping mechanism is characterized by the individual using physical activity or exercise to manage stress?

    A. Sublimation
    B. Suppression
    C. Deflection
    D. Displacement

24. How does the oncology certified nurse contribute to the continuity of care within the interdisciplinary team in end-of-life care?

    A. Monitoring patients' vital signs and administering medications
    B. Documenting patients' preferences and care plans accurately
    C. Performing psychological assessments to address emotional needs
    D. Collaborating with healthcare providers to develop treatment plans

25. Jane, a 52-year-old breast cancer patient undergoing chemotherapy, is interested in using herbal supplements for symptom management. She mentions that her friend recently started taking a specific herbal supplement and experienced significant pain relief. Jane asks the nurse for advice regarding the use of herbal supplements. Which of the following is the most appropriate response by the nurse?

    A. "Herbal supplements can have potential benefits, but it is crucial to consult with your healthcare team before starting any new treatment. They can assess possible interactions with your chemotherapy."
    B. "There is limited evidence supporting the effectiveness of herbal supplements in managing cancer symptoms. Instead, I recommend trying other evidence-based interventions like massage or acupuncture."
    C. "Herbal supplements are not recommended for cancer patients, as they can interfere with chemotherapy and cause serious side effects."
    D. "You can try herbal supplements, but it is important to remember that they are not regulated by the FDA and may be ineffective or even harmful."

26. John, a 45-year-old male, is undergoing treatment for prostate cancer. During a routine visit, he tells you that he has been feeling overwhelmed and hopeless lately. He expresses thoughts of ending his life and states that he sees no reason to continue living. What is the most appropriate nursing action in this situation?

    A. Ensure John's immediate safety by activating the appropriate suicide prevention protocols.
    B. Encourage John to talk about his feelings with his family and close friends.

C. Suggest John engage in meaningful activities to distract him from his negative thoughts.

D. Ask John if he has previously tried any self-harm methods or has access to any means of suicide.

27. Mr. Wilson, a 68-year-old lung cancer patient, is scheduled for a multidisciplinary team meeting to discuss his treatment plan. The oncology certified nurse will be an active participant in this meeting. What is the primary role of the nurse during this meeting?

A. Offer emotional support to Mr. Wilson and his family members.

B. Act as a liaison between different healthcare professionals involved in Mr. Wilson's care.

C. Document the treatment plan and decisions made during the meeting.

D. Provide education to Mr. Wilson about the various treatment options available.

28. Mr. Johnson, a 65-year-old male with advanced lung cancer, is undergoing radiation therapy. Which statement about the effects of radiation on the immune system is accurate?

A. Radiation therapy can cause neutropenia, predisposing patients to infections.

B. Radiation therapy enhances the production of T cells.

C. Radiation has no impact on lymphocyte count or function.

D. Radiation stimulates the production of antibodies.

29. Which statement about survivorship rehabilitation is accurate?

A. Survivorship rehabilitation focuses only on physical health.

B. Survivorship rehabilitation is only appropriate during active cancer treatment.

C. Survivorship rehabilitation aims to improve survivor's quality of life.

D. Survivorship rehabilitation focuses primarily on end-of-life care.

30. Which of the following measures is used to calculate the incidence rate of a disease in a population?

    A. Prevalence Rate
    B. Relative Risk
    C. Odds Ratio
    D. Attack Rate

31. Scenario-based a patient named Sarah, who is 57 years old and has breast cancer, presents to the emergency department with symptoms of fever, chills, nausea, and confusion. Her vital signs include a temperature of 39.5°C (103.1°F), heart rate of 110 bpm, respiratory rate of 28 breaths per minute, and blood pressure of 88/52 mmHg. Lab results show a white blood cell count of 18,000/mml and a lactate level of 4 mmol/L. What intervention should the nurse prioritize for this patient?

    A. Administer Antibiotics
    B. Provide Fluid Resuscitation
    C. Initiate Oxygen Therapy
    D. Obtain Blood Cultures

32. Mrs. Thomas, a 56-year-old female, has been recently diagnosed with breast cancer. Her healthcare provider explains the staging and histological grading of her cancer. Mrs. Thomas is confused about these terms and asks the nurse to provide further clarity. Which of the following options reflects the correct definition of staging and histological grading in relation to cancer?

    A. Staging refers to the size and spread of the tumor, while histological grading determines the aggressiveness of cancer cells..
    B. Staging assesses the response to cancer treatment, while histological grading evaluates the likelihood of cancer recurrence.
    C. Staging determines the tumor location, while histological grading determines the genetic mutations present in cancer cells.
    D. Staging identifies the cancer type, while histological grading determines the presence of metastatic disease.

33.   Emma, a 32-year-old transgender woman, is receiving chemotherapy for breast cancer. She expresses concerns about the potential side effects of the treatment on her gender transition. As her oncology nurse, what is the most appropriate response?

    A. "Don't worry about your transition right now. Focus on your cancer treatment."
    B. "Your concerns are valid. Let's discuss the potential side effects and explore strategies to manage them."
    C. "Gender transition is not a priority during cancer treatment. You should postpone it for now."
    D. "I understand your worries, but we can't modify the treatment plan. It's best to prioritize your cancer treatment."

34.   Sarah, a 38-year-old woman, underwent a bilateral mastectomy for breast cancer six months ago. She is now in the survivorship phase and has recently started dating someone new. She has concerns about how her partner will react to her physical appearance and whether she can still experience sexual pleasure. As her oncology nurse, what information would you provide to address Sarah's concerns?

    A. Share information about breast reconstruction options and suggest counseling for body image issues.
    B. Reassure Sarah that her partner will accept her as she is and recommend seeking therapy to address anxiety.
    C. Educate Sarah on the importance of maintaining a healthy lifestyle and its positive effects on sexual function.
    D. Advise Sarah to avoid sexual activities and focus on emotional intimacy instead.

35.   Mrs. Thomas, a 62-year-old female, is diagnosed with bladder cancer. She is undergoing chemotherapy and experiencing urinary incontinence as a side effect. Which nursing intervention should be prioritized to manage her urinary incontinence?

    A. Encouraging Mrs. Thomas to limit fluid intake
    B. Recommending Kegel exercises
    C. Providing absorbent pads

D. Administering antispasmodic medication

36. Which of the following is an appropriate nursing intervention for addressing financial concerns in oncology patients?

    A. Provide information on community resources for financial assistance
    B. Encourage patients to avoid discussing financial matters with healthcare providers
    C. Advise patients to prioritize medical bills over other expenses
    D. Discourage patients from seeking financial counseling and support groups

37. Which of the following best describes the term 'discrimination concerns' in survivorship care?

    A. The provision of equal access to healthcare services for all cancer survivors.
    B. The process of recognizing the unique needs and challenges of cancer survivors.
    C. Offering support and resources to cancer survivors during the transition to follow-up care.
    D. Addressing prejudicial treatment or negative experiences faced by cancer survivors due to their diagnosis.

38. Which statement best describes the impact of social relationships and family dynamics on the psychosocial well-being of oncology patients?

    A. Social relationships and family dynamics have no effect on the psychosocial well-being of oncology patients.
    B. Only positive social relationships have an impact on the psychosocial well-being of oncology patients.
    C. Negative social relationships and family dynamics can contribute to increased depression and anxiety in oncology patients.
    D. The psychosocial well-being of oncology patients is solely determined by individual factors unrelated to social relationships or family dynamics.

39. Which medication is commonly used for the relief of breakthrough cancer pain in oncology patients?

    A. Acetaminophen
    B. Gabapentin
    C. Amitriptyline
    D. Fentanyl

40. Mrs. Sullivan, a 72-year-old patient with metastatic lung cancer, is admitted to the oncology unit for end-of-life care. She is experiencing dyspnea and anxiety. The nurse is implementing non-pharmacologic comfort measures to alleviate her symptoms. Which intervention would be most appropriate in this situation?

    A. Administering low-dose opioids to manage dyspnea
    B. Providing oxygen therapy via nasal cannula to improve oxygen saturation
    C. Teaching relaxation techniques such as deep breathing and guided imagery
    D. Encouraging family members to visit less frequently to reduce stress levels

41. Mrs. Johnson, a 58-year-old woman, has been diagnosed with terminal pancreatic cancer. She tells the nurse that she fears dying and leaving her husband alone. She expresses concerns about how he will manage without her. The nurse recognizes these statements as indications of which stage of grief?

    A. Denial
    B. Anger
    C. Depression
    D. Acceptance

42. Which of the following statements about Superior vena cava (SVC) syndrome is correct?

    A. SVC syndrome is predominantly caused by bronchial carcinoma.
    B. SVC syndrome is commonly associated with peripheral edema.

C. SVC syndrome typically presents with decreased jugular venous distention.

D. SVC syndrome is often managed with thrombolytic therapy.

43. Anxiety is a common psychosocial distress experienced by patients with cancer. Which of the following interventions would be most appropriate for managing anxiety in these patients?

A. Encouraging the patient to avoid discussing their fears and concerns.

B. Administering benzodiazepines on a scheduled basis to promote relaxation.

C. Teaching deep breathing exercises and progressive muscle relaxation techniques.

D. Restricting the patient's access to information about their cancer treatment.

44. Mrs. Johnson, a 40-year-old breast cancer survivor, comes to the oncology clinic for her routine follow-up appointment. During her visit, she expresses concerns about her increased fatigue and lack of motivation. She mentions feeling overwhelmed and isolated. Mrs. Johnson is experiencing:

A. Oncologic Emergencies
B. Late Effects of Cancer Treatment
C. Emotional Distress
D. Long-Term Survivorship Issues

45. Which of the following is a non-modifiable risk factor for developing cancer?

A. Smoking
B. Exposure to environmental toxins
C. Age
D. Sedentary lifestyle

46. Sarah, a 45-year-old woman, has been receiving chemotherapy for the past six months to treat her breast cancer. She now complains of persistent numbness and tingling in her hands and feet. Upon examination, Sarah exhibits decreased sensation in her extremities. Which of the following chronic side effects is most likely responsible for these symptoms?

     A. Peripheral neuropathy
     B. Cardiotoxicity
     C. Nephrotoxicity
     D. Hepatotoxicity

47. Emma, a 35-year-old woman, was diagnosed with breast cancer. After completing her treatment, she is eager to return to work and resume her normal routine. Emma works at a small startup company that does not provide health insurance coverage. She is concerned about how this may affect her ability to secure health insurance coverage due to her medical history. Which of the following statements is correct regarding Emma's employment and health insurance?

     A. Emma is guaranteed health insurance coverage regardless of her medical history.
     B. Emma can be denied health insurance coverage due to her pre-existing condition.
     C. Ernma is eligible for health insurance coverage through her employer, as mandated by the Affordable Care Act.
     D. Ermma can only obtain health insurance coverage through a government program like Medicaid or Medicare.

48. Which of the following risk factors is NOT associated with depression?

     A. History of substance abuse
     B. Family history of depression
     C. Chronic illness or pain
     D. Low socioeconomic status

49.   Which musculoskeletal alteration is a common manifestation in patients with metastatic bone disease?

   A. Pathological fractures
   B. Osteoporosis
   C. Rheumatoid arthritis
   D. Paget's disease of bone

50.   Which of the following rehabilitation interventions is most commonly used for cancer survivors to improve physical functioning and quality of life?

   A. Yoga and meditation
   B. Physical therapy
   C. Cognitive-behavioral therapy
   D. Art therapy

51.   Tracy is a 45-year-old patient who is undergoing chemotherapy for breast cancer. She has been experiencing nausea, vomiting, and a loss of appetite, which has resulted in weight loss and muscle wasting. As her oncology certified nurse, you are responsible for managing her nutrition and providing appropriate interventions. Which of the following recommendations would be most appropriate to improve Tracy's nutritional status?

   A. Encourage Tracy to eat large, heavy meals to meet her caloric needs.
   B. Suggest Tracy eat small, frequent meals that are easy to digest and nutrient-dense.
   C. Advise Tracy to avoid all types of foods to prevent triggering her nausea and vomiting.
   D. Recommend Tracy to limit her fluid intake to prevent further weight loss.

52.   What is an example of a surgical intervention commonly used in the treatment of cancer?

   A. Radical mastectorny
   B. Radiation therapy
   C. Chemotherapy

D. Targeted therapy

53.   Which of the following immune cells is responsible for directly recognizing and killing cancer cells?

A. B cells
B. T cells
C. Natural killer cells
D. Neutrophils

54.   Which of the following is a normal grief reaction during the bereavement process?

A. Expressing anger or guilt towards the deceased.
B. Feeling intense happiness and relief.
C. Resuming normal activities within a few days.
D. Experiencing a sense of emptiness and sadness.

55.   Which of the following strategies is an example of a preventive health practice in the context of health promotion and disease prevention?

A. Encouraging individuals to engage in regular physical activity.
B. Promoting smoking cessation programs for individuals with lung cancer.
C. Providing palliative care for patients with terminal cancer.
D. Educating individuals about the benefits of a balanced diet.

56.   Mrs. Johnson is the primary caregiver for her husband who is undergoing treatment for lung cancer. She has been experiencing overwhelming tiredness, feelings of guilt, and a loss of interest in activities she once enjoyed. Which of the following interventions would be the most appropriate to help alleviate caregiver fatigue in Mrs. Johnson?

A. Encourage her to take breaks throughout the day to rest and engage in activities she finds enjoyable.
B. Advise her to put the needs of her husband before her own and continue providing care without interruption.

C. Suggest she increase her caffeine intake to boost energy levels and combat fatigue.

D. Recommend attending caregiver support group meetings to discuss feelings and gain insights from others.

57. Mrs. Johnson, a 55-year-old patient with acute myeloid leukemia (AML), recently underwent an allogeneic stem cell transplant. She is now at a high risk of developing graft- versus-host disease (GVHD). The nurse performs an assessment and identifies which of the following as an early sign of acute GVHD?

A. Diarrhea
B. Fatigue
C. Weight gain
D. Hair loss

58. Which pharmacologic comfort measure is commonly used to manage severe pain in patients receiving end-of-life care?

A. Nonsteroidal anti-inflammatory drugs (NSAIDs)
B. Local anesthetics
C. Opioids
D. Antidepressants

59. A 48-year-old woman with no family history of breast cancer presents to the community health clinic for her annual check-up. During the assessment, the nurse identifies a small, painless lump in the upper, outer quadrant of her left breast. The patient reports that she does not have any other breast changes or symptoms. What should the nurse's priority action be?

A. Reassure the patient that the lump is likely benign and instruct her to monitor it for any changes.

B. Refer the patient to a breast specialist for further evaluation and possible biopsy.

C. Order a mammogram to assess the lump and determine if additional testing is needed.

D. Educate the patient about breast self-examination and provide a pamphlet with instructions.

60.   Mr. Anderson, a 55-year-old patient diagnosed with lung cancer, is scheduled to undergo a bronchoscopy with biopsy. The nurse prepares the patient for the procedure and provides preoperative instructions. Which instruction should the nurse provide to the patient?

A. NPO (nothing by mouth) for 8 hours prior to the procedure
B. Restrict fluid intake for 24 hours prior to the procedure
C. Take the routine medications with a small sip of water
D. Apply a topical anesthetic to the throat before the procedure

61.   John, a 55-year-old man with prostate cancer, has been feeling down and hopeless for several weeks. He has difficulty concentrating and often experiences fatigue. The nurse suspectsthat John may be experiencing symptoms of depression. Which of the following actions should the nurse take initially?

A. Assens if John has a family history of depression
B. Encourage John to participate in support groups with other cancer patients.
C. Evaluate John's vital signs to rule out any physical causes of his symptoms
D. Provide John with information about relaxation techniques and coping strategies.

62.   Mrs. Johnson, a 65-year-old oncology patient, is about to start her chemotherapy treatment. The nurse is discussing the treatment plan with her. Mrs. Johnson expresses her concerns about understanding the treatment schedule and managing potential side effects. She mentions that reading medical information makes her anxious and prefers visual aids to understand complex topics. What would be the most appropriate educational approach for Mrs. Johnson?

A. Provide her with written brochures and pamphlets about chemotherapy treatment.
B. Explain the treatment plan using illustrations, diagrams, and visual aids.
C. Encourage her to join a support group to learn from other patients experiences.
D. Recommend online articles and websites for self-study.

63. Maria, a 45-year-old woman, was recently diagnosed with breast cancer. She expresses feeling overwhelmed, restless, and having difficulty sleeping. During the assessment, the nurse finds that Maria is experiencing excessive worry and has an elevated heart rate. Which intervention by the nurse is most appropriate?

    A. Encouraging Maria to practice deep breathing exercises.
    B. Administering an anti-anxiety medication immediately.
    C. Advising Maria to ignore her feelings and focus on positive thoughts.
    D. Suggesting Maria participate in a support group once a month.

64. Mrs. Johnson, a 60-year-old female diagnosed with small cell lung cancer, presents with dyspnea, facial swelling, and dilated veins on her chest and neck. On physical examination, you note engorged jugular veins, edema of the face and upper extremities, and prominent chest veins. Mrs. Johnson reports a worsening cough and difficulty swallowing. What is the most appropriate nursing intervention for Mrs. Johnson?

    A. Administer anticoagulant therapy.
    B. Encourage the patient to lie flat.
    C. Elevate the head of the bed.
    D. Perform a cardiac stress test.

65. Which laboratory finding is indicative of sepsis in an oncology patient?

    A. Increased white blood cell count.
    B. Increased platelet count.
    C. Decreased lactate levels.
    D. Decreased C-reactive protein levels.

66. Which intervention is recommended for managing lymphedema in oncology patients?

    A. Avoiding limb movement to prevent further swelling
    B. Applying tight bandages or compression garments to the affected limb
    C. Avoiding fluid intake to minimize lymph flow
    D. Massaging the affected limb vigorously

67. Lisa, an Oncology Certified Nurse, has recently been promoted to a leadership position in the oncology unit. She wants to implement a new evidence-based practice to improve patient outcomes. Which action should Lisa take to ensure successful implementation and acceptance of the new practice by the nursing staff?

    A. Implement the practice without seeking input from the nursing staff.
    B. Provide clear explanations and educational sessions on the benefits of the new practice to the nursing staff.
    C. Delegate the responsibility of implementing the new practice to another nurse on the team.
    D. Ignore any resistance or concerns raised by the nursing staff and focus on the benefits of the new practice.

68. Which of the following statements is true regarding the scope of practice for an Oncology Certified Nurse?

    A. The nurse's scope of practice includes prescribing chemotherapy medications
    B. The nurse's scope of practice encompasses providing emotional support to patients and their families
    C. The nurse's scope of practice involves performing radiation therapy procedures
    D. The nurse's scope of practice allows for administering anesthesia during surgical procedures

69. David, a 62-year-old patient with metastatic melanoma, has been receiving combination immunotherapy treatment with anti-PD-1 and anti-CTLA-4 antibodies. During a routine follow-up visit, David mentions experiencing persistent diarrhea for the past week. He denies any abdominal pain or blood in the stool. Laboratory tests reveal a normal stool culture and negative Clostridium difficile toxin. What is the most likely cause of David's diarrhea?

    A. Colitis
    B. Pancreatitis
    C. Hepatitis

D. Gastritis

70. Jane is a 45-year-old patient with a recent diagnosis of breast cancer. She is scheduled to undergo a modified radical mastectomy tomorrow. The nurse is preparing to provide preoperative care to Jane. Which statement by the nurse demonstrates adherence to standards of care in the nursing process?

    A. "I will administer pain medication before surgery to ensure Jane's comfort."
    B. "I will document Jane's vital signs every two hours during her postoperative recovery."
    C. "I will encourage Jane to verbalize her fears and concerns about the surgery."
    D. "I will educate Jane about the importance of quitting smoking."

71. Which of the following site-specific considerations is not associated with breast cancer?

    A. Lymphedema
    B. Bone metastasis
    C. Ascites
    D. Paget's disease

72. Emily, a 55-year-old female patient, has been diagnosed with breast cancer. After conducting various tests, the oncologist determines that the cancer cells have not spread beyond the breast and nearby lymph nodes. Based on this information, what is the most appropriate classification of Emily's breast cancer?

    A. Stage 0
    B. Stage I
    C. Stage II
    D. Stage III

73. Mr. Davis, a 52-year-old patient diagnosed with leukemia, has been receiving treatment from his wife who acts as the primary caregiver. She has been experiencing significant caregiver fatigue. Which approach is most appropriate in managing caregiver fatigue in this situation?

    A. Scheduling weekly counseling sessions for the caregiver to address emotional needs.
    B. Encouraging the caregiver to solely focus on her husband's care to avoid involvement in other activities.
    C. Providing information on the latest research regarding leukemia treatment options.
    D. Recommending the caregiver attend educational sessions on managing stress and self-care techniques.

74. Which of the following is an important consideration when discussing advance care planning with a patient?

    A. Explaining the benefits of alternative medicine for cancer treatment
    B. Encouraging the patient to delay making decisions until they are close to end of life
    C. Promoting open communication and informed decision-making
    D. Recommending aggressive treatment options for all cancer diagnoses

75. John, a 50-year-old patient with metastatic breast cancer, has been prescribed biotherapy as part of his treatment plan. Which of the following statements about biotherapy is correct?

    A. Biotherapy involves the use of medications that target specific molecules in cancer cells.
    B. Biotherapy refers to the use of radiation therapy to treat cancer.
    C. Biotherapy is exclusively used in the management of hematologic malignancies.
    D. Biotherapy is ineffective in treating solid tumors.

76. Which of the following is consistent with the standard of practice for an Oncology Certified Nurse?

    A. Adhering to the principles of evidence-based practice by integrating research findings into patient care
    B. Administering high-dose chemotherapy without appropriate physician orders
    C. Providing treatment recommendations without collaborating with the interdisciplinary healthcare team
    D. Neglecting to maintain accurate and up-to-date patient documentation

77. Josh is a 60-year-old man who has been recently diagnosed with lung cancer. He has just begun chemotherapy and is experiencing significant hair loss. He expresses feelings of embarrassment and self-consciousness about his appearance to the Oncology Certified Nurse (OCN). Question: Which nursing intervention would be most appropriate to provide psychosocial support to Josh?

    A. Discuss the benefits of wearing a wig or head coverings.
    B. Encourage Josh to focus on the positive aspects of treatment.
    C. Recommend joining a lung cancer support group.
    D. Facilitate communication with family and friends.

78. Which intervention is appropriate for supporting bereaved individuals?

    A. Encouraging complete avoidance of emotions.
    B. Minimizing their feelings of grief.
    C. Providing emotional support and active listening.
    D. Urging quick resolution of mourning process.

79. Mr. Williams, a 68-year-old man with advanced pancreatic cancer, is admitted to the palliative care unit. He presents with profound fatigue, anorexia, and generalized muscle weakness. As his oncology nurse, you recognize that alterations in functioning can significantly impact a patient's ability to perform daily activities. Which of the following nursing interventions would be most appropriate for managing Mr. Williams' alterations in functioning?

    A. Implementing a high-protein diet to improve muscle strength.
    B. Administering erythropoietin to address anemia.
    C. Teaching energy conservation techniques.
    D. Initiating chemotherapy to target cancer cells.

80. Sarah, an Oncology Certified Nurse, has been assigned as the charge nurse for the oncology unit. She is responsible for managing the unit, ensuring patient safety, and coordinating care among the nursing staff. One day, Sarah notices that one of the nurses on her team consistently arrives late for her shift, causing delays in patient care. What leadership action should Sarah take to address this issue?

    A. Confront the nurse publicly and reprimand her for her behavior.
    B. Ignore the issue and hope that it resolves on its own.
    C. Schedule a private meeting with the nurse to discuss the problemn and find a solution together.
    D. Assign the nurse to a different shift without discussing the issue.

81. Which of the following is a preferred learning style for oncology patients?

    A. Auditory
    B. Kinesthetic
    C. Visual
    D. Analytical

82. John, a 60-year-old male with a diagnosis of lung cancer, complains of severe neck pain radiating to his upper extremities. He also experiences weakness and difficulty in coordination. On physical examination, there is decreased sensation and strength in his upper extremities. An MRI confirms the presence of spinal cord compression at the level of C5. What should be the primary nursing action for John?

    A. Provide a neck collar and educate the patient on proper immobilization
    B. Administer corticosteroids to reduce inflammation and swelling
    C. Assist the patient with range-of-motion exercises for the neck
    D. Prepare for immediate surgical decompression of the spinal cord

83. Which of the following statements about hospice care is correct?

    A. Hospice care focuses on providing curative treatments for patients with terminal illnesses.
    B. Hospice care is provided only in hospitals and medical facilities.
    C. Hospice care primarily focuses on improving the quality of life for patients with life-limiting illnesses.
    D. Hospice care is provided for an indefinite period until the patient's condition stabilizes.

84. Emily is an Oncology Certified Nurse working in a busy oncology unit. She has noticed a pattern of increased medication errors being reported by her colleagues. Emily believes that a lack of training and knowledge about new medications may be causing these errors. What action should Emily take to address this issue?

    A. Request additional training sessions on new medications for the nursing staff.
    B. Keep silent and hope that the situation resolves on its own.
    C. Assign blame to individual nurses who made the errors.
    D. Implement a new policy requiring double-checking of all medications.

85. Mr. Johnson, a 62-year-old patient with terminal pancreatic cancer, has been under hospice care for the past month. During a routine assessment, the nurse notices that the patient's family seems overwhelmed and emotionally exhausted. What intervention would be most appropriate for the nurse to implement in this situation?

    A. Suggesting the family attend a support group for caregivers.
    B. Encouraging the family to take a short break from caregiving.
    C. Providing information about respite care services.
    D. Arranging a family meeting with the hospice team.

86. Ms. Anderson, a 55-year-old female, is admitted to the oncology unit with Small Cell Lung Cancer. Her laboratory reports show hyponatremia, concentrated urine, and increased urine osmolality. The oncologist suspects Syndrome of Inappropriate Antidiuretic Hormone Secretion (SIADH). Which of the following interventions should the nurse prioritize?

    A. Administering intravenous hypertonic saline solution.
    B. Restricting fluid intake.
    C. Initiating diuretic therapy.
    D. Administering intravenous normal saline solution.

87. Emily, a 35-year-old woman with a history of breast cancer, has recently completed her treatment and has been in remission for the past six months. She and her partner are considering starting a family but are concerned about the potential risks of pregnancy due to her previous cancer diagnosis and treatment. They seek your advice regarding contraception options. Which of the following contraceptive methods would you recommend for Emily?

    A. Combined oral contraceptives (COCs)
    B. Intrauterine device (IUD)
    C. Barrier methods (e.g., condoms)
    D. Fertility awareness-based methods (FABMs)

88. Which of the following clinical manifestations is typical of pneumonitis in cancer patients?

A. Hemoptysis
B. Rapid weight gain
C. Peripheral cyanosis
D. Epigastric pain

89. Which surgical procedure is used to remove a malignant tumor from the breast?

A. Mastectomy
B. Hysterectomy
C. Colectomy
D. Prostatectomy

90. Mr. Anderson, a 68-year-old man with lung cancer, is receiving palliative care at home. His daughter, Sarah, is his primary caregiver. Sarah expresses feelings of guilt for not being able to fulfill all her father's needs along with managing her own family. Which of the following nursing interventions should the nurse prioritize to support Sarah?

A. Collaborate with community resources to provide respite care for Sarah.
B. Advise Sarah to prioritize her own family's needs over her father's care.
C. Educate Sarah on the importance of managing all of her father's needs herself.
D. Discourage Sarah from expressing her feelings of guilt, as it may negatively impact her father's well-being.

91. A patient with cancer who is experiencing cachexia should be encouraged to

A. Limit protein intake.
B. Increase intare of high fat foods.
C. Engage in regular physical exercise.
D. Reduce overall calorie consumption.

92.   Which of the following is a classic manifestation of hypercalcemia in patients with cancer?

A. Hypertension
B. Hypotension
C. Constipation
D. Diarrhea

93.   Sarah, a 45-year-old female, was diagnosed with breast cancer and underwent mastectomy surgery. She is concerned about the possibility of developing lymphedema. Which intervention should the nurse implement to reduce the risk of lymphedema in Sarah?

A. Encourage Sarah to use creams and lotions on her arms and chest.
B. Teach Sarah to elevate her arm on a pillow while resting or sleeping.
C. Advise Sarah to avoid any physical activity involving the affected arm.
D. Instruct Sarah to perform vigorous exercises to improve lymphatic flow.

94.   Mr. Anderson, a 66-year-old male with a history of lung cancer, presents to the oncology clinic with complaints of fatigue, dyspnea, and recent-onset tachycardia. On physical examination, jugular venous distention, muffled heart sounds, and pulsusparadoxus are noted. An echocardiogram reveals an enlarged pericardial effusion with echocardiographic signs of impending tamponade. Which of the following findings is consistent with impending cardiac tamponade?

A. Decreased central venous pressure (CVP)
B. Normal blood pressure
C. Prolonged QT interval on ECG
D. Elevated jugular venous pressure (JVP)

95. Mrs. Johnson is a 65-year-old patient with breast cancer who is undergoing chemotherapy. She is experiencing nausea and vomiting, which is affecting her appetite and overall nutrition. Which intervention is most appropriate for managing her symptoms and promoting adequate nutrition?

    A. Encouraging the patient to eat large, heavy meals to ensure adequate calorie intake.
    B. Advising the patient to avoid all foods and drinks that she thinks might trigger her nausea.
    C. Prescribing a medication such as ondansetron to relieve her nausea and improve appetite.
    D. Recommending the patient to consume high-fat foods to compensate for the decreased appetite.

96. Mrs. Johnson, a 65-year-old patient diagnosed with advanced lung cancer, resides with her husband. The husband has been the primary caregiver and has been facing caregiver fatigue. Which intervention could be most effective in alleviating caregiver fatigue in this situation?

    A. Encouraging respite care and providing information on local support groups for caregivers.
    B. Providing education on the importance of exercise and physical activity.
    C. Suggesting relaxation techniques, such as deep breathing exercises and meditation.
    D. Recommending an additional caregiving responsibility for the couple's adult child.

97. Which of the following factors increase the risk of developing venous thromboembolism (VTE) in oncology patients?

    A. Advanced age and obesity
    B. Regular physical activity
    C. Low dose chemotherapy
    D. Adequate hydration

98.   Mr. Thomas, a 58-year-old male with metastatic lung cancer, is admitted to the oncology unit. He presents with sudden dyspnea, chest pain, and hemoptysis. The nurse suspects a pulmonary embolism and initiates diagnostic testing. The pulmonary angiography confirms the diagnosis, and disseminated intravascular coagulation (DIC) is suspected as a complication. Which of the following mursing interventions should be prioritized for Mr. Thomas?

A. Administer oxygen therapy.
B. Administer thrombolytic therapy.
C. Administer anticoagulation therapy.
D. Administer corticosteroids.

99.   Mr. Thomas is a 72-year-old patient with advanced pancreatic cancer on palliative care. He has been experiencing severe pain. Which of the following medications would be the most appropriate choice for effective pain management in Mr. Thomas?

A. Hurufen 200mg every & hours
B. Acetaminophen 500mg as needed.
C. Morphine sulfate immediate-release 5mg every 4 hours.
D. DJ Codeine phosphate 10mg every 6 hours.

100.   Mrs. Anderson, a 52-year-old patient with breast cancer, is receiving chemotherapy with paclitaxel. During the administration of the medication, she develops difficulty breathing, facial swelling, and hives. What type of hypersensitivity reaction is Mrs. Anderson experiencing?

A. Type I hypersensitivity reaction
B. Type II hypersensitivity reaction
C. Type III hypersensitivity maction
D. Type IV hypersensitivity reaction

101. John, a 60-year-old male patient with advanced lung cancer, is admitted to the oncology unit for palliative care. He has been experiencing severe pain related to his cancer and requests pain medications frequently. As an oncology nurse, what action aligns best with the scope and standards of practice in oncology nursing?

    A. Administer pain medications only as prescribed by the health-care provider.
    B. Implement alternative therapies, such as acupuncture, to manage John's pain.
    C. Educate John about the importance of non-pharmacological pain. management techniques.
    D. Collaborate with the interdisciplinary team to develop an individual-ized pain management plan for John.

102. Nancy is a 62-year-old Hispanic female diagnosed with breast cancer. She recently immigrated to the United States and speaks limited English. The oncology nurse is providing education to Nancy about her treatment options. Which action by the nurse best demonstrates culturally con-gruent care?

    A. Using medical jargon while explaining Nancy's treatment plan.
    B. Providing written materials only in English for Nancy to review.
    C. Requesting an interpreter to help communicate with Nancy.
    D. Assuming Nancy's understanding based on non-verbal cues.

103. Which of the following best describes the concept of evidence-based practice in oncology nursing?

    A. Relying solely on personal opinions and experiences when making clinical decisions.
    B. Incorporating patient preferences and values into decision-making.
    C. Following established guidelines and protocols without question.
    D. Providing care based on the nurse's intuition and instincts.

104. Which of the following is an appropriate nursing intervention for a patient experiencing complicated grief?

    A. Encouraging the patient to suppress and avoid acknowledging their feelings of grief.
    B. Assisting the patient in finding support groups and counseling services.
    C. Discouraging the patient from expressing their emotions openly.
    D. Minimizing the patient's grief and emphasizing the need to move on quickly.

105. Which of the following is true regarding the process of carcinogenesis?

    A. It is a reversible process.
    B. Mutations are not involved in carcinogenesis.
    C. Radiation and chemical exposure have no influence on carcinogenesis.
    D. Carcinogenesis involves the conversion of normal cells into cancer cells.

106. Which type of symptom is characterized by a sudden onset and typically resolves within a short period of time?

    A. Acute symptom
    B. Chronic symptom
    C. Late symptom
    D. Asymptomatic

107. Which procedure involves the surgical removal of the testicles to treat testicular cancer?

    A. Orchiectomy
    B. Nephrectomy
    C. Cholecystectomy
    D. Appendectomy

108. Which of the following services are typically included in hospice care?

    A. Aggressive medical interventions to prolong life.
    B. Experimental treatments and therapies.
    C. Bereavement support for the patient's family.

D. Curative treatments aimed at reversing the illness.

109. Mr. Jenkins, a 58-year-old patient diagnosed with stage IV lung cancer, is undergoing treatment for his condition. The healthcare provider informs him about the possibility of cancer metastasis and explains the common sites for metastasis in lung cancer. Which of the following options represents a common metastatic location for lung cancer?

    A. Liver
    B. Kidneys
    C. Pancreas
    D. Spleen

110. Samantha, a 45-year-old woman, has been diagnosed with advanced ovarian cancer. She is devastated by the news and expresses concerns about losing control over her life. She worries about the impact of her illness on her family, her career, and her ability to make decisions regarding her treatment. Samantha is anxious and feels helpless. Which intervention would be most appropriate for the nurse to implement?

    A. Encouraging Samantha to express her feelings and concerns openly.
    B. Administering anxiety medication to help calm Samantha down.
    C. Advising Samantha to avoid thinking about her illness and focus on other activities.
    D. Suggesting that Samantha take a break from her treatment regime.

111. Which of the following is an example of emotional support for a patient undergoing cancer treatment?

    A. Providing information about the treatment options.
    B. Assisting with personal care activities.
    C. Organizing transportation to medical appointments.
    D. Offering a listening ear and empathy.

112. Which of the following statements regarding the scientific basis of oncology nursing practice is true?

    A. Oncology nursing practice is solely focused on providing emotional support to cancer patients.
    B. The scientific basis of oncology nursing practice requires understanding the genetic factors contributing to cancer development.
    C. The scientific basis of oncology nursing practice does not involve the use of evidence-based guidelines for patient care.
    D. Oncology nursing practice does not require an understanding of the physiological changes associated with cancer.

113. Which of the following alterations in cardiac function is commonly observed in patients undergoing chemotherapy?

    A. Hypertension
    B. Bradycardia
    C. Cardiomyopathy
    D. Tachypnea

114. Mr. Anderson, a 38-year-old male patient with a family history of colorectal cancer, is scheduled for genetic counseling and testing. He asks the nurse how genetic testing can help detect the presence of cancer. What would be the most appropriate response by the nurse?

    A. "Genetic testing helps to identify changes in specific genes that are associated with an increased risk of developing colorectal cancer."
    B. "Genetic testing can determine the effectiveness of the current cancer treatment and guide further interventions."
    C. "Genetic testing assesses the symptoms and helps in the diagnosis of colorectal cancer."
    D. "Genetic testing can identify the stage of cancer and provide prognostic information."

115. Which of the following is a presenting sign of septic shock in a patient with cancer?

    A. Hypotension
    B. Bradycardia
    C. Hypertension
    D. Bradypnea

116. Which of the following changes in cognition is commonly seen in cancer patients undergoing chemotherapy?

    A. Memory deficits.
    B. Increased attention span.
    C. Heightened problem-solving skills.
    D. Improved language abilities.

117. John, a 45-year-old African American male, is receiving chemotherapy for colorectal cancer. During a routine assessment, the oncology nurse notices that John seems withdrawn and avoids making eye contact. Which action by the nurse demonstrates culturally congruent care?

    A. Ignoring John's non-verbal cues as a cultural norm.
    B. Assuming John is uninterested in discussing his concerns.
    C. Encouraging John's family to participate in his care.
    D. Asking open-ended questions to enquire about John's emotional well-being.

118. Jane, a 50-year-old woman, completed her chemotherapy for breast cancer three months ago. She is now scheduled for a follow-up appointment with her oncologist. During the visit, Jane mentions that she has been experiencing persistent fatigue and difficulty sleeping. The oncologist suspects this may be related to her previous treatment. Which action should the nurse prioritize when discussing Jane's concerns?

    A. Recommend a sleep study to identify any underlying sleep disorders.
    B. Educate Jane on the importance of incorporating regular exercise into her routine.
    C. Assess Jane's emotional well-being and psychological distress levels.

D. Schedule a consultation with a nutritionist to evaluate Jane's dietary habits.

119.   Which of the following strategies can help alleviate the financial concerns of cancer patients?

A. Encouraging patients to avoid discussing their financial worries with healthcare providers.
B. Advising patients to delay seeking medical help due to financial constraints.
C. Connecting patients with financial resources and community support programs.
D. Suggesting patients bear the financial burden on their own without seeking assistance.

120.   A 45-year-old female patient, Mrs. Johnson, has recently undergone a mastectomy due to breast cancer. She expresses concerns about her altered body image to the oncology nurse. Which nursing intervention would be most appropriate for addressing Mrs. Johnson's psychological needs?

A. Providing information about reconstructive surgery options.
B. Recommending a support group for cancer survivors.
C. Encouraging Mrs. Johnson to hide her surgical scar with clothing.
D. Advising Mrs. Johnson to avoid looking at herself in the mirror.

121.   Which of the following is a key consideration for providing palliative care to patients with advanced cancer?

A. Pain Management.
B. Chemotherapy Administration.
C. Experimental Treatments.
D. Disease Eradication.

122. Sarah, a 48-year-old woman, was diagnosed with breast cancer two months ago. She has been undergoing chemotherapy and radiation therapy as part of her treatment. Recently, she has been feeling increasingly sad and anxious. She has difficulty sleeping and has lost interest in activities she used to enjoy. What is the most appropriate action for the nurse to take in this situation?

    A. Provide emotional support and refer Sarah to a mental health professional.
    B. Advise Sarah to find a support group for cancer survivors.
    C. Encourage Sarah to engage in relaxation techniques, such as deep breathing exercises.
    D. Suggest Sarah take up a new hobby to distract herself from negative emotions.

123. Which of the following statements best describes the impact of cancer treatment on the sexual health of patients?

    A. Cancer treatment rarely affects the sexual health of patients.
    B. Patients undergoing cancer treatment often experience improved sexual function.
    C. Cancer treatment can have varying effects on the sexual health of patients.
    D. Cancer treatment always has a positive impact on the sexual health of patients.

124. Which of the following are common triggers for anaphylaxis in oncology patients?

    A. Chemotherapy drugs
    B. Contrast media used in imaging studies
    C. Blood transfusions
    D. All of the above

125. When assessing a patient for depression, which screening tool is frequently used by healthcare professionals?

    A. Hamilton Rating Scale for Depression (HAM-D)

B. Geriatric Depression Scale (GDS)
C. Beck Depression Inventory (BDI)
D. Patient Health Questionnaire (PHQ-9)

126. Which alteration in functioning is commonly observed in oncology patients undergoing chemotherapy?

    A. Increased sense of smell and taste sensitivity.
    B. Hypersomnia and excessive daytime sleepiness.
    C. Peripheral neuropathy and numbness/tingling in extremities.
    D. Hypertension and elevated blood pressure readings.

127. Mr. Johnson, a 65-year-old male diagnosed with prostate cancer, will be receiving radiation therapy as part of his treatment plan. He expresses concerns about the potential side effects of radiation therapy. As the oncology certified nurse, which response would be most appropriate?

    A. "Radiation therapy is a safe treatment option with no side effects."
    B. "Radiation therapy may cause fatigue, skin changes, and urinary problems. However, these are usually temporary and can be managed with appropriate interventions."
    C. "Radiation therapy will only cause mild discomfort, such as a sunburn-like effect on the skin."
    D. "Radiation therapy has no side effects if the treatment is administered correctly."

128. Which of the following immune cells is involved in cell-mediated immunity and is responsible for attacking and destroying infected cells?

    A. Macrophages
    B. T lymphocytes
    C. Eosinophils
    D. Basophils

129. Mrs. Johnson, a 58-year-old patient, recently completed radiation therapy for breast cancer. She is concerned about the risk of developing a subsequent malignancy and seeks clarification from the oncology nurse. Which of the following statements by the nurse is correct regarding subsequent malignancies?

    A. "There is no evidence to suggest a higher risk of subsequent malignancies after radiation therapy."
    B. "Radiation therapy increases the risk of developing subsequent malignancies in nearby healthy tissues."
    C. "Chemotherapy increases the risk of subsequent malignancies more than radiation therapy."
    D. "Only patients who received both radiation therapy and chemotherapy are at risk for subsequent malignancies."

130. Samantha is a 35-year-old breast cancer survivor who has just completed her treatment. She is concerned about the impact of her cancer treatment on her sexual health. She is experiencing vaginal dryness and pain during intercourse. Samantha discusses her concerns with her oncology nurse, who provides education on managing these concerns. Which of the following options would be the most appropriate advice for the nurse to give Samantha?

    A. Use over-the-counter vaginal moisturizers.
    B. Avoid sexual activity until all treatment side effects subside.
    C. Use petroleum jelly as a lubricant during intercourse.
    D. Seek therapy for coping with sexual concerns.

131. What is a common symptom of unresolved grief?

    A. Rapid acceptance of the loss and moving on without difficulty.
    B. Expression of emotions and open communication about the loss.
    C. Inability to engage in regular activities and loss of interest in previously enjoyed hobbies.
    D. Seeking support from friends and family members to cope with grief.

132. Sarah, a 45-year-old female patient with breast cancer, presents to the oncology clinic for follow-up. She is scheduled to receive chemotherapy in the next few weeks. The nurse performs an assessment and notices that Sarah has developed a fever of 101°F (38.3°C), reports fatigue, and complains of a sore throat. Which action by the nurse is appropriate based on the scope and standards of oncology nursing practice?

    A. Administer prescribed chemotherapy as scheduled.
    B. Refer Sarah to an infectious disease specialist for further evaluation.
    C. Advise Sarah to rest and take over-the-counter medications for her symptoms.
    D. Contact Sarah's oncologist to report the findings and follow their guidance.

133. Which of the following factors plays a significant role in determining the prognosis of site-specific cancers?

    A. Tumor size and stage.
    B. Patient's age and gender.
    C. Family history of cancer.
    D. Dietary preferences and lifestyle choices.

134. Tumor lysis syndrome (TLS) is a potential oncologic emergency that can occur during the treatment of certain cancers. Which of the following statements about TLS is correct?

    A. TLS is most commonly seen in solid tumors.
    B. TLS is characterized by decreased levels of uric acid.
    C. TLS can be prevented by limiting fluid intake.
    D. TLS is associated with the release of intracellular contents into the bloodstream.

135. Which of the following is not a typical symptom of spinal cord compression?

    A. Back pain
    B. Muscle weakness

    C. Bowel incontinence

    D. High fever

136. Which of the following is a common metastatic location for breast cancer?

    A. Liver

    B. Colon

    C. Bladder

    D. Pancreas

137. Which is a common stage of grief experienced during bereavement?

    A. Denial

    B. Anger

    C. Acceptance

    D. Bargaining

138. Which of the following complications is associated with the use of vascular access devices (VADs) for treatment administration?

    A. Catheter dislodgement

    B. Hypertension

    C. Hyperglycemia

    D. Visual disturbances

139. Which of the following actions is a violation of the legal and ethical principles related to documentation in oncology nursing practice?

    A. Documenting patient assessments and interventions accurately and objectively.

    B. Altering or falsifying patient records to cover up errors or negligence.

    C. Keeping patient information confidential and secure.

    D. Using appropriate medical terminology in documentation.

140. Which of the following is an appropriate nursing intervention to help manage cognitive changes in cancer patients receiving palliative care?

    A. Encouraging independence in self-care activities.

B. Providing complex problem-solving tasks.
C. Limiting interaction with family and friends.
D. Minimizing environmental stimuli.

141.   Which of the following is a common metastatic location for lung cancer?

A. Kidneys
B. Stomach
C. Bones
D. Thyroid

142.   Which of the following is NOT a typical symptom of superior vena cava syndrome (SVCS)?

A. Facial edema
B. Dyspnea
C. Hoarseness
D. Hemoptysis

143.   Ms. Johnson, a 49-year-old patient with breast cancer, is scheduled to undergo surgery next week. Her surgeon has recommended the use of a wound dressing with honey for her post-operative wound care. As the oncology nurse, what is your role in this situation?

A. Advocate for the use of an alternative wound dressing.
B. Comply with the surgeon's recommendation and apply the honey dressing.
C. Research the evidence regarding the use of honey dressings for post-operative wound care.
D. Consult the patient's family for their opinion on the wound dressing.

144.   Which symptom is commonly associated with neurological alterations in oncology patients?

A. Visual disturbances
B. Nausea and vomiting
C. Fatigue

D. Anorexia

145. Which communication technique would be most appropriate for the nurse to use when addressing Sarah's concerns?

   A. Asking closed-ended questions
   B. Providing medical jargon.
   C. Active listening.
   D. Avoiding eye contact.

146. Susan has symptoms of intracranial pressure (ICP). Which intervention is the highest priority for Susan at this time?

   A. Administering opioids for pain relief.
   B. Assisting with lumbar puncture.
   C. Elevating the head of the bed to 30 degrees.
   D. Administering high-flow oxygen via a non-rebreather mask.

147. Mrs. Thompson, a 65-year-old patient with advanced pancreatic cancer, has been admitted to the unit. She is experiencing severe pain and is considering different treatment options for her condition. During a discussion with the nurse, the topic of advanced care planning comes up. Which of the following best describes advanced care planning?

   A. Advanced care planning is a legal document that outlines the medical treatments a patient wishes to receive or avoid if they become unable to make decisions.
   B. Advanced care planning is the process of discussing treatment options with the healthcare team and making informed decisions about which treatments to pursue.
   C. Advanced care planning is a process that involves predicting the patient's prognosis and outlining a care plan accordingly.
   D. Advanced care planning is a document that specifies the person who will make medical decisions on behalf of the patient if they become unable to do so.

148. Which of the following factors is NOT a risk factor for the development of cardiovascular diseases?

    A. Smoking
    B. Sedentary lifestyle
    C. High intake of fruits and vegetables
    D. Hypertension

149. Sarah, a 45-year-old female, is receiving chemotherapy for breast cancer. She is concerned about the potential impact on her immune system. Which of the following statements about the immune system is accurate?

    A. Chemotherapy has no effect on the immune system.
    B. Chemotherapy may weaken the immune system, increasing the risk of infections.
    C. Chemotherapy enhances the function of the immune system.
    D. Chemotherapy has minimal impact on the immune system, it primarily affects other body systems.

150. Lisa, a 45-year-old female, has been receiving chemotherapy for breast cancer. She completed her treatment six months ago. During her follow-up appointment, she reports persistent fatigue, difficulty concentrating, and memory problems. Which of the following chronic side effects is Lisa most likely experiencing?

    A. Peripheral neuropathy
    B. Lymphedema
    C. Chemobrain
    D. Cardiac toxicity

151. Which action should the oncology certified nurse take to address discrimination concerns in survivorship care?

    A. Educate the healthcare team about the importance of cultural sensitivity and diversity training.
    B. Ignore discrimination concerns as they are not directly related to the medical aspect of survivorship.

C. Advise patients to ignore incidents of discrimination and focus on their medical treatment.

D. Report discrimination concerns to the patient's family members to seek their assistance.

152. Which intervention is most appropriate for a patient experiencing altered body image after undergoing surgery for the removal of a tumor in the breast?

A. Encouraging the patient to express feelings of sadness and grief related to changes in body image.

B. Providing education about postoperative exercises to help regain strength and mobility.

C. Recommending the use of a prosthetic breast to restore balance and symmetry.

D. Referring the patient to a support group for individuals who have undergone similar surgical procedures.

153. Emma, a 57-year-old woman, has recently been diagnosed with breast cancer. She is scheduled to undergo a mastectomy next week. As an oncology certified nurse, you provide pre-operative education to Emma regarding site-specific cancer considerations. Which of the following statements is true regarding breast cancer surgery?

A. Radiation therapy is always necessary after a mastectomy.

B. In breast-conserving surgery, the entire breast is removed.

C. Sentinel lymph node biopsy is a common procedure performed during breast cancer surgery.

D. Systemic chemotherapy is not a recommended treatment option for breast cancer.

154. Which of the following statements accurately describes the legal protection of an Oncology Certified Nurse's practice?

    A. The nurse's practice is protected only within the confines of the hospital setting.
    B. The nurse is legally protected to practice independently without physician oversight.
    C. The nurse is accountable for maintaining licensure and practicing in accordance with state laws and regulations.
    D. The nurse is exempt from legal action in the event of substandard care.

155. Which type of vascular access device (VAD) is most suitable for long-term treatment administration?

    A. Peripherally Inserted Central Catheter (PICC)
    B. Tunneled Central Venous Catheter (CVC)
    C. Implanted Port
    D. Peripheral Intravenous Catheter (PIV)

156. Which of the following statements about family and social support concerns in oncology is true?

    A. Family and social support concerns have no impact on the survivorship and care continuum.
    B. Family and social support play a minor role in the emotional well-being of cancer survivors.
    C. A lack of family and social support can negatively affect the overall quality of life for cancer survivors.
    D. Family and social support concerns are solely the responsibility of healthcare professionals.

157. Mrs. Johnson, a 62-year-old female, is receiving palliative care for advanced lung cancer. She presents with increasing dyspnea and a nonproductive cough. Upon auscultation, you hear bilateral coarse crackles over both lung fields. Mrs. Johnson's oxygen saturation is 82% on room air. Which intervention should the nurse prioritize to alleviate Mrs. Johnson's respiratory distress?

    A. Administering nebulized bronchodilators.
    B. Initiating supplemental oxygen therapy.
    C. Encouraging Mrs. Johnson to perform pursed-lip breathing.
    D. Providing postural drainage and percussion techniques.

158. Collaboration is an essential component in oncology nursing practice. Which of the following best defines collaboration in the context of oncology nursing?

    A. Collaboration refers to the exchange of information and ideas between healthcare professionals to develop a plan of care for oncology patients.
    B. Collaboration involves working independently and making decisions without involving other healthcare team members.
    C. Collaboration refers to seeking advice from only oncologists and excluding other healthcare professionals in patient care.
    D. Collaboration is the process of performing nursing interventions without seeking input from other healthcare professionals.

159. Which of the following is an appropriate nursing intervention for Sarah's grief?

    A. Encouraging Sarah to avoid expressing her emotions to maintain a positive mindset.
    B. Suggesting Sarah to isolate herself from her support system to process her grief alone.
    C. Providing a safe and nonjudgmental environment for Sarah to express her emotions freely.
    D. Discouraging Sarah from seeking professional counseling to deal with her grief.

160. Mrs. Anderson, a 62-year-old female with advanced breast cancer, is receiving chemotherapy. During her most recent treatment, she develops a sudden onset of shortness of breath, wheezing, and a rash. The nurse suspects a hypersensitivity reaction. What type of hypersensitivity reaction is most likely occurring in this patient?

    A. Type I hypersensitivity reaction
    B. Type II hypersensitivity reaction
    C. Type III hypersensitivity reaction
    D. Type IV hypersensitivity reaction

161. Which of the following best represents the concept of quality of practice in oncology nursing?

    A. Adherence to evidence-based guidelines.
    B. Managerial skills in organizing patient care.
    C. Demonstration of compassionate patient interactions.
    D. Proficiency in performing technical procedures.

162. Which of the following statements best describes evidence-based practice in oncology nursing?

    A. Evidence-based practice focuses on the use of traditional nursing practices without incorporating research findings.
    B. Evidence-based practice involves using individual clinical expertise and patient preferences in conjunction with the best available research evidence.
    C. Evidence-based practice utilizes only research evidence without considering individual clinical expertise or patient preferences.
    D. Evidence-based practice relies solely on personal beliefs and values to guide nursing care.

163. Sarah is a 45-year-old patient who is receiving chemotherapy for breast cancer. She has completed one round of treatment and is scheduled for her second round next week. During the first round of chemotherapy, Sarah experienced severe fatigue and nausea, resulting in multiple visits to the emergency department for supportive care. As the oncology certified nurse, you are responsible for ensuring efficient resource utilization. Which of the following interventions would be most appropriate for managing Sarah's symptoms and reducing unnecessary emergency department visits?

    A. Educating Sarah about potential side effects and self-management strategies.
    B. Recommending that Sarah discontinue chemotherapy due to intolerable side effects.
    C. Encouraging Sarah to limit her physical activity to conserve energy.
    D. Referring Sarah to a psychiatrist for evaluation of underlying mental health issues.

164. According to the psychosocial dimensions of care, what is an important factor to consider when addressing intimacy with cancer patients?

    A. Providing education on sexual health resources.
    B. Encouraging abstinence throughout the treatment process.
    C. Discouraging open communication about sexual concerns.
    D. Avoiding the topic of intimacy altogether.

165. Olivia, a 45-year-old woman with ovarian cancer, is concerned about the financial burden of her cancer treatment. She is particularly worried about the cost of her chemotherapy drugs. Which resource would be most appropriate to assist Olivia in obtaining financial support for her treatment?

    A. Local cancer support groups.
    B. Government-funded assistance programs.
    C. Hospital-based financial assistance programs.
    D. Private insurance providers.

Answer Key

Q.	1	2	3	4	5	6	7	8	9	10	11	12	13	14
A.	A	A	D	A	A	A	B	C	A	C	C	C	A	A

Q.	15	16	17	18	19	20	21	22	23	24	25	26	27	28
A.	A	A	C	C	B	D	C	B	A	B	A	A	B	A

Q.	29	30	31	32	33	34	35	36	37	38	39	40	41	42
A.	C	D	B	A	B	A	B	A	D	C	D	C	C	A

Q.	43	44	45	46	47	48	49	50	51	52	53	54	55	56
A.	C	C	C	A	B	C	A	B	B	A	C	D	A	A

Q.	57	58	59	60	61	62	63	64	65	66	67	68	69	70
A.	A	C	B	A	C	B	A	C	A	B	B	B	A	C

Q.	71	72	73	74	75	76	77	78	79	80	81	82	83	84
A.	C	A	D	C	A	A	A	C	C	C	C	D	C	A

Q.	85	86	87	88	89	90	91	92	93	94	95	96	97	98
A.	D	B	B	A	A	A	C	C	B	D	C	A	A	C

Q.	99	100	101	102	103	104	105	106	107	108	109	110	111	112
A.	C	A	D	C	B	B	D	A	A	C	A	A	D	B

Q.	113	114	115	116	117	118	119	120	121	122	123	124	125	126
A.	C	A	A	A	D	C	C	B	A	A	C	D	D	C

Q.	127	128	129	130	131	132	133	134	135	136	137	138	139	140
A.	B	B	B	A	C	D	A	D	D	A	B	A	B	D

Q.	141	142	143	144	145	146	147	148	149	150	151	152	153	154
A.	C	D	C	A	C	C	A	C	B	C	A	C	C	C

Q.	155	156	157	158	159	160	161	162	163	164	165
A.	C	C	B	A	C	A	A	B	A	A	B

Answers and Explanations

1.   A: When confirming prostate cancer, a transrectal ultrasound (TRUS)-guided biopsy is considered the gold standard diagnostic measure.

2.   A: Regular use of sunscreen is an important preventive health practice to reduce the risk of developing skin cancer.

3.   D: Radiation-

4.   A: Collaborating with Jonathan to develop a schedule that allows him to be involved in his care is the most appropriate intervention.

5.   A: The symptoms of dyspnea, cough, chest pain, and decreased breath sounds on physical examination, along with the presence of a pleural effusion, are indicative of pneumonitis.

6.   A: Providing education on self-care techniques and stress management is a crucial intervention in supporting caregivers. Emily needs to understand the importance of taking care of her own physical and emotional well-being while caring for her sister.

7.   B: Tachycardia is a common sign of increased intracranial pressure (ICP) and reflects the body's compensatory response to maintain cerebral perfusion.

8.   C: The scientific basis of oncology nursing practice involves a commitment to evidence-based care and continuous improvement.

9.   A: Chronic lung cancer-associated symptoms primarily develop due to long-term exposure to cigarette smoke, leading to chronic inflammation in the lungs. This inflammation can trigger persistent cough, dyspnea (shortness of breath), wheezing, and in advanced cases, clubbing of fingers.

10.   C: Social support is a coping mechanism that entails seeking comfort, advice, or assistance from others in times of distress. This mechanism recognizes the importance of interpersonal connections and the benefits of sharing emotions with trusted individuals. Rationalization involves

providing logical explanations or justifications to reduce anxiety. Denial is the refusal to accept or acknowledge a distressing reality. Intellectualization involves the excessive use of rational reasoning to avoid the emotional aspects of a situation.

11. C: Xerostomia, or dry mouth, is a common side effect of chemotherapy. Spicy and acidic foods can exacerbate the dryness and discomfort experienced by patients with xerostomia.

12. C: Innate immunity represents the first line of defense against pathogens and is not considered an adaptive immune response. It includes physical barriers (e.g., skin), chemical barriers (e.g., stomach acid), and cellular components (e.g., neutrophils).

13. A: When conducting a clinical trial for oncology patients, obtaining informed consent from the participants is crucial. Informed consent involves providing comprehensive information to patients about the nature of the study, its potential risks and benefits, their rights, and the right to withdraw at any time without repercussions. It ensures that patients have a thorough understanding of the trial before agreeing to participate, promotes autonomy, and protects their rights.

14. A: Staging refers to determining the extent of cancer spread, while histological grading assesses the degree of differentiation of tumor cells. In this case, Mr. Johnson's tumor has invaded through the colon wall but has not spread to nearby lymph nodes or distant sites, indicating Stage II. The histological grade of moderate differentiation corresponds to Grade 2.

15. A: Massage therapy involves the manipulation of soft tissues through applying pressure, tension, or vibration to specific areas of the body. It is often used in oncology care to provide pain relief, reduce anxiety, and improve overall well-being. Massage therapy helps to relax muscles, promote blood circulation, and release endorphins, which can help patients manage pain and alleviate symptoms associated with cancer treatment.

16. A: Platelet count is a crucial laboratory value to monitor during chemotherapy administration.

17. C: Weight gain is not a characteristic symptom of depression. Instead, changes in appetite and weight loss are more commonly observed in individuals suffering from depression.

18. C: The statement that Mrs. Sanchez will need to avoid sun exposure during radiation treatment indicates a need for further clarification. While it is generally recommended to protect the treated area from direct sun exposure, it does not mean complete avoidance of sun exposure. Sunscreen with a high SPF can be used, and brief sun exposure may be permitted. The other statements are all accurate and appropriate..

19. B: When a patient enrolled in a clinical trial experiences severe adverse reaction to the experimental treatment, the immediate priority is to ensure patient safety. The nurse should stop the administration of the treatment and assess the patient's condition to determine the severity of the reactions and provide appropriate interventions. While it is important to inform the principal investigator, document the adverse reactions, and report them to the institutional review board, the primary concern is the immediate well-being of the patient.

20. D: The primary role of an oncology nurse in patient advocacy is to support and represent the best interests of the patients. This involves advocating for their rights, ensuring their preferences and values are respected, and providing comprehensive and compassionate care. Nurses act as the patients' voice, ensuring that all decisions and interventions align with their well-being and individual needs.

21. C: Providing culturally competent care involves understanding and addressing the unique needs and concerns of individuals from diverse backgrounds. Asking John if he has a sexual partner shows sensitivity to his sexual orientation and opens the opportunity to provide him with information about support services specifically designed for the LGBTQ+ community. This approach acknowledges and respects his identity, facilitating comprehensive care and support throughout his hospital stay.

22.   B: Patients who have previously had cancer are at increased risk of developing subsequent malignancies, with a higher likelihood of occurring in the same organ or site as the initial cancer.

23.   A: Sublimation is a coping mechanism that involves the redirection of negative or socially unacceptable emotions into constructive behaviors, such as physical activity or exercise. This allows individuals to manage their stress by channeling their energy into healthier outlets.

24.   B: In the interdisciplinary team for end-of-life care, the oncology certified nurse plays a vital role in ensuring the continuity of care. One of the key responsibilities is accurately documenting patients' preferences, goals of care, and care plans. This documentation helps facilitate effective communication among team members, ensuring that all healthcare providers are aware of the individualized needs of patients.

25.   A: The nurse acknowledges the potential benefits of herbal supplements while emphasizing the importance of consulting with the healthcare team. This response promotes patient autonomy, encourages collaborative decision-making, and highlights the need for healthcare professionals to evaluate any potential interactions between herbal supplements and chemotherapy. Patient safety is prioritized, ensuring appropriate guidance and monitoring regarding the use of complementary modalities alongside conventional cancer treatment.

26.   A: When a patient expresses thoughts of ending their life, it is crucial to prioritize their safety. Activating suicide prevention protocols, which may include involving mental health professionals or notifying appropriate authorities, ensures immediate support and intervention to prevent harm.

27.   B: The primary role of an oncology certified nurse during a multidisciplinary team meeting is to act as a liaison between different healthcare professionals.

28.   A: Radiation therapy can suppress the bone marrow, causing a decrease in the production of neutrophils, leading to neutropenia. This leaves patients susceptible to infections.

29. C: Survivorship rehabilitation is a comprehensive approach that aims to improve the overall quality of life for cancer survivors. It focuses not only on physical health but also addresses emotional, psychological, and social aspects of survivorship. It is applicable throughout the cancer journey, spanning from diagnosis to post-treatment. Survivorship rehabilitation helps survivors in managing treatment-related side effects, enhancing functional abilities, and promoting overall well-being. End-of-life care is not the primary focus of survivorship rehabilitation.

30. D: The attack rate is a measure used to calculate the incidence rate of a disease in a population during an outbreak or an epidemic. It is calculated by dividing the number of new cases of the disease by the total population at risk during a specified time period. The attack rate helps determine the risk of acquiring the disease in the population and is particularly useful in infectious disease epidemiology. Prevalence rate refers to the proportion of individuals with a disease at a given time, while relative risk and odds ratio are used to measure associations between exposures and outcomes in analytical epidemiological studies.

31. B: The patient's symptoms and vital signs indicate sepsis and possible septic shock, which is a medical emergency. The nurse's priority intervention should be to provide fluid resuscitation to address the hypotension and hypoperfusion associated with septic shock.

32. A: Staging is a process that assesses the size of the tumor, degree of local invasion, and presence of metastases to determine the extent and spread of cancer in the body. It helps in planning appropriate treatment strategies and predicting prognosis. Histological grading involves evaluating the appearance and differentiation of cancer cells under a microscope. It classifies cancer cells into different grades based on their resemblance to normal cells and determines the aggressiveness of the tumor. This information is crucial in guiding treatment decisions and predicting the likelihood of cancer progression.

33. B: By acknowledging the patient's concerns and offering to discuss the potential side effects, the nurse demonstrates a patient-centered approach.

34.   A: Share information about breast reconstruction options and suggest counseling for body image issues. By offering these resources, the nurse supports Sarah's journey towards acceptance and helps her explore options to enhance her self-esteern and sexual well-being after breast cancer treatment.

35.   B: Kegel exercises, also known as pelvic floor exercises, strengthen the pelvic floor muscles, which can improve bladder control and reduce urinary incontinence. These exercises target the muscles responsible for controlling urine flow and are an effective strategy in managing stress incontinence, which is commonly seen as a side effect of chemotherapy.

36.   A: As an oncology nurse, it is important to address the psychosocial dimensions of care, including financial concerns. Providing information on community resources for financial assistance can help alleviate the financial burden experienced by oncology patients.

37.   D: Addressing prejudicial treatment or negative experiences faced by cancer survivors due to their diagnosis.

38.   C: Social relationships and family dynamics play a crucial role in the psychosocial well-being of oncology patients.

39.   D: Fentanyl is a potent opioid analgesic commonly used for the management of severe breakthrough cancer pain.

40.   C: I Teaching relaxation techniques such as deep breathing and guided imagery can help Mrs. Sullivan achieve a sense of calmness, decrease anxiety levels, and improve her breathing patterns. This intervention focuses on promoting Mrs. Sullivan's comfort and enhancing her quality of life during the end-of-life care phase.

41.   C: The depression stage of grief.

42.   A: Superior vena cava (SVC) syndrome occurs when there is obstruction of blood flow through the SVC. It is most commonly caused by bronchial carcinoma, accounting for about 70% of cases.

43. C: Teaching deep breathing exercises and progressive muscle relaxation techniques can help patients with cancer manage their anxiety effectively. These techniques promote relaxation, reduce muscle tension, and decrease physiological symptoms associated with anxiety.

44. C: Mrs. Johnson's symptoms of increased fatigue, lack of motivation, feeling overwhelmed, and isolated indicate emotional distress rather than oncologic emergencies, late effects of cancer treatment, or long-term survivorship issues.

45. C: Age is a non-modifiable risk factor because as individuals grow older, the risk of developing cancer increases.

46. A: The persistent numbness and tingling in Sarah's hands and feet along with the decreased sensation in her extremities are suggestive of peripheral neuropathy, which is a common chronic side effect of chemotherapy.

47. B: Emma can be denied health insurance coverage due to her pre-existing condition, because she works for a small company. Prior to the implementation of the Affordable Care Act, health insurance companies could deny coverage or charge higher premiums based on an individual's pre-existing conditions. Although the law prohibits such practices, small companies with less than 50 employees are exempt from this requirement.

48. C: Chronic illness or pain can contribute to psychosocial distress, but is not associated with depression.

49. A: Pathological fractures are a common manifestation in patients with metastatic bone disease.

50. B: Physical therapy is a widely used rehabilitation intervention for cancer survivors to improve physical functioning and overall quality of life.

51. B: Chemotherapy often results in gastrointestinal side effects such as nausea, vomiting, and loss of weight and malnutrition. Encouraging Tracy to eat small, frequent meals that are easy to digest and are nutrient-dense can help manage her symptoms while providing nutrients to support her

nutritional status. This approach allows Tracy to maintain her caloric intake despite her reduced appetite and can minimize gastrointestinal distress caused by heavy meals.

52. A: Radical mastectomy is a surgical procedure that involves removal of the breast tissue and nearby lymph nodes. It is often performed in cases of invasive breast cancer to remove the tumor and surrounding tissues.

53. C: Natural killer (NK) cells are a type of lymphocyte that plays a vital role in immune surveillance against cancer cells.

54. D: During the bereavement process, it is normal for individuals to experience a sense of emptiness and sadness. Grief is a natural response to loss, and these feelings are commonly observed.

55. A: Regular physical activity is a preventive health practice as it helps reduce the risk of developing various chronic diseases, such as heart diseases, type 2 diabetes, and certain types of cancer.

56. A: Encouraging Mrs. Johnson to take breaks throughout the day to rest and engage in activities she finds enjoyable is the most appropriate intervention to alleviate caregiver fatigue. Caregivers often neglect their own needs, leading to physical and emotional exhaustion. Taking regular breaks and pursuing pleasurable activities can help rejuvenate and prevent burnout.

57. A: Acute graft-versus-host disease (GVHD) commonly occurs within the first 100 days post-transplant. It is an inflammatory response of donor T cells attacking the recipient's organs, commonly affecting the skin, gastrointestinal(GI) tract, and liver. Diarrhea is an early sign of acute GVHD, accompanied by abdominal cramping, nausea, and anorexia.

58. C: Opioids are the cornerstone of managing severe pain in patients receiving end-of-life care. They provide effective pain relief by acting on the central nervous system to alter the perception and response to pain.

59.   B: In this scenario, the nurse identifies a palpable lump in the patient's breast. While benign breast lumps are common and can occur throughout the menstrual cycle, a thorough evaluation by a specialist is necessary to rule out malignancy. Referring the patient to a breast specialist for further evaluation and possible biopsy is the appropriate priority action in accordance with evidence-based practice guidelines.

60.   A: NPO (nothing by mouth) for 8 hours prior to the procedure.

61.   C: It is essential to initially evaluate John's vital signs to rule out any physical causes of his symptoms, such as anemia or hormonal imbalances, that may mimic depression symptoms. Depression assessment should include ruling out physical causes before considering psychological factors.

62.   B: Explain the treatment plan using illustrations, diagrams, and visual aids. This approach can enhance her understanding and reduce anxiety related to reading complex medical information.

63.   A: Deep breathing exercises are an effective non-pharmacological intervention for managing anxiety.

64.   C: Elevating the head of the bed helps to alleviate the symptoms of superior vena cava syndrome (SVCS) by reducing venous congestion and facilitating venous return. This position decreases the pressure exerted on the superior vena cava, thus reducing the severity of symptoms.

65.   A: Increased white blood cell count. While not always reliable, an increased white blood cell (WBC) count is commonly observed in sepsis, reflecting the body's attempt to fight off the infection.

66.   B: The recommended intervention for managing lymphedema in oncology patients is to apply tight bandages or compression garments to the affected limb. This helps to improve lymphatic flow, reduce swelling, and provide support.

67.   B: Provide clear explanations and educational sessions on the benefits of the new practice to the nursing staff. As a leader, Lisa should involve the

nursing staff in the decision-making process to gain their support and improve acceptance of the new practice.

68. B: As an Oncology Certified Nurse, providing emotional support to patients and their families is an essential aspect of the nurse's scope of practice. This includes listening to patients' concerns, addressing their emotional needs, and offering guidance and resources to cope with the challenges of cancer.

69. A: The combination of anti-PD-1 and anti-CTLA-4 antibodies can lead to immune-related colitis as a side effect. Diarrhea is one of the common manifestations. It is essential to assess the severity of colitis and initiate appropriate management promptly to prevent complications such as bowel perforation or sepsis.

70. C: By encouraging Jane to verbalize her fears and concerns about the surgery, the nurse addresses her emotional well-being. This allows for effective communication, support, and identification of any potential psychosocial factors that may impact her surgical experience. Providing emotional support is a crucial aspect of the nursing process and reflects the standards of care for oncology nursing practice.

71. C: Ascites refers to the accumulation of fluid in the abdominal cavity, which is not typically associated with breast cancer.

72. A: Stage 0 is the earliest stage of breast cancer, also known as carcinoma in situ. It means that abnormal cells are present but have not spread to nearby tissues or lymph nodes. In this case, the cancer is confined to the ducts or lobules of the breast without invading nearby normal tissue.

73. D: Recommending the caregiver attend educational sessions on managing stress and self-care techniques.

74. C: When discussing advance care planning, it is crucial to promote open communication and informed decision-making with the patient. This involves providing information about the available treatment options, potential outcomes, and the patient's right to make choices about their care.

75. A: Biotherapy involves the use of medications that target specific molecules in cancer cells.

76. A: The standard of practice for an Oncology Certified Nurse includes adhering to evidence-based practice by incorporating the latest research findings into patient care.

77. A: Discussing the benefits of wearing a wig or head coverings would provide the most appropriate psychosocial support to Josh, who is feeling self-conscious about hair loss. This intervention addresses his specific concern and offers a solution to help him regain confidence in his appearance.

78. C: When providing care for bereaved individuals, it is essential to provide emotional support. Active listening, empathy, and validation of their feelings play a crucial role in promoting healing and helping them adjust to the loss.

79. C: Teaching energy conservation techniques.

80. C: As a leader, Sarah should approach this situation in a professional and respectful manner. By scheduling a private meeting with the nurse, Sarah can address the problem directly, understand the reasons behind the tardiness, and collaboratively find a solution.

81. C: Visual.

82. D: The presence of severe neck pain, radiating symptoms, and neurological deficits indicates spinal cord compression. The primary nursing action should be preparing for immediate surgical decompression of the spinal cord to alleviate the compression and prevent further neurological damage.

83. C: Hospice care is a specialized form of end-of-life care that aims to provide comfort and support to individuals with terminal illnesses.

84. A: As a professional practice evaluator, Emily has recognized a potential issue affecting patient safety. Requesting additional training sessions on

new medications for the nursing staff is the most appropriate action to address the root cause of the increased medication errors.

85.   D: In this scenario, the most appropriate intervention for the nurse to implement would be arranging a family meeting with the hospice team. This meeting can provide an opportunity for the family to express their concerns, understand the progression of the disease, and explore available support services.

86.   B: In SIADH, there is excessive production and release of antidiuretic hormone (ADH), leading to water retention, dilutional hyponatremia, and concentrated urine. The nurse should prioritize fluid restriction to prevent further water retention and hyponatremia.

87.   B: Intrauterine device (IUD) Given Emily's history of breast cancer, it is important to consider her hormonal status and potential interactions with contraception. COCs, which contain estrogen, might not be the ideal choice as estrogens could potentially stimulate cancer cell growth.

88.   A: Hemoptysis, or coughing up blood, is a common presentation of pneumonitis in cancer patients. This can occur due to damage to the blood vessels within the lung tissue.

89.   A: Mastectomy is a surgical procedure that involves the removal of the entire breast, including the breast tissue and sometimes the surrounding lymph nodes. It is commonly performed as a treatment option for breast cancer.

90.   A: Caregiver burden is common among family caregivers, and it is crucial to support them in their role. Collaborating with community resources to provide respite care will allow Sarah to take breaks and attend to her own family's needs, reducing her feelings of guilt and preventing burnout. By addressing Sarah's needs, the nurse indirectly supports Mr. Anderson's well-being by ensuring his primary caregiver is emotionally and physically capable of providing high-quality care.

91.   C: Engage in regular physical exercise. Cachexia is a complex metabolic syndrome associated with cancer, characterized by weight loss, muscle wasting, and loss of appetite. Engaging in regular physical exercise can help improve muscle strength and muscle mass.

92.   C: Hypercalcemia in patients with cancer can present with a variety of symptoms, including neuromuscular irritability, anorexia, nausea, vomiting, polyuria, polydipsia, and constipation.

93.   B: Elevating the affected arm on a pillow while resting or sleeping helps to promote lymphatic drainage and reduce the risk of lymphedema.

94.   D: Elevated jugular venous pressure (JVP)

95.   C: Ondansetron is a medication used to treat nausea and vomiting caused by chemotherapy. By addressing the patient's symptoms, ondansetron can improve her appetite and overall nutrition.

96.   A: Caregiver fatigue is a common issue faced by individuals providing care for cancer patients. Encouraging respite care allows the primary caregiver to take a break from caregiving responsibilities and engage in self-care.

97.   A: Advanced age and obesity are significant risk factors for developing venous thromboembolism (VTE) in oncology patients.

98.   C: When a thromboembolic event like pulmonary embolism causes DIC, the nurse should prioritize administering anticoagulation therapy. Anticoagulation with heparin helps prevent further clot formation and promotes the resolution of existing clots.

99.   C: Morphine sulfate immediate-release 5mg every 4 hours.

100.   A: Type I hypersensitivity reaction

101.   D: Collaborate with the interdisciplinary team to develop an individualized pain management plan for John.

102. C: Requesting an interpreter to help communicate with Nancy.

103. B: Incorporating patient preferences and values into decision-making. Evidence-based practice is an essential component of quality oncology nursing practice. It involves integrating the best available evidence, patient preferences, and clinical expertise when making clinical decisions.

104. B: Assisting the patient in finding support groups and counseling services. Complicated grief refers to an intense and prolonged form of grief that may impair an individual's ability to function.

105. D: Carcinogenesis is the process by which normal cells are transformed into cancer cells. It is a complex, multifactorial process involving genetic, epigenetic, and environmental factors.

106. A: Acute symptoms refer to those that appear suddenly and have a short duration.

107. A: Orchiectomy is the surgical removal of one or both testicles and is commonly performed as a treatment for testicular cancer.

108. C: Bereavement support for the patient's family.

109. A: Lung cancer often metastasizes to the liver due to its abundant blood supply and direct venous drainage from the lungs. As such, oncology-certified nurses need to be aware of these common sites for metastatic spread in order to provide appropriate care and support to the patients. Identifying common metastatic locations helps direct intervention and monitoring, facilitating earlier detection and intervention if necessary.

110. A: Encouraging Samantha to express her feelings and concerns openly is the most appropriate intervention.

111. D: Emotional support plays a crucial role in the psychosocial care of cancer patients. It emphasizes the importance of actively listening to patients' feelings and demonstrating empathy, which helps them feel understood and supported during their cancer journey.

112. B: In order to provide effective care to patients with cancer, oncology nurses must have a solid understanding of the scientific basis of the disease. This includes knowledge of the genetic factors that contribute to cancer development and progression. By understanding these genetic factors, nurses can tailor patient care, treatments, and interventions accordingly. This knowledge also enables nurses to educate patients and their families about hereditary risks, genetic testing, and personalized medicine options.

113. C: Cardiomyopathy refers to the deterioration of the heart muscle, leading to decreased cardiac function. It is a known risk associated with certain chemotherapeutic agents, such as anthracyclines.

114. A: Genetic testing is crucial for identifying mutations in genes like APC linked to a higher risk of colorectal cancer. Detection of these mutations can help in assessing an individual's predisposition to the disease, determining the need for additional screenings or preventive strategies, and providing genetic counseling to the patient and their family members. It enables personalized management plans that consider the increased risk and potential interventions to reduce the likelihood of developing colorectal cancer.

115. A: In septic shock, systemic vasodilation and increased capillary permeability lead to hypotension. This results from the complex interplay of pro-inflammatory mediators released in response to infection.

116. A: One common alteration in cognition seen in cancer patients undergoing chemotherapy is memory deficits. Chemotherapy can lead to cognitive impairment, commonly referred to as chemo brain, which is characterized by problems with memory, attention, and concentration. Patients may experience difficulty in remembering names, dates, and appointments.

117. D: Asking open-ended Qquestions to enquire about John's emotional well-being.

118. C: Assess Jane's emotional well-being and psychological distress levels.

119. C: Connecting patients with financial resources and community support programs.

120. B: Recommending a support group for cancer survivors would be the most appropriate nursing intervention to address Mrs. Johnson's altered body image.

121. A: When providing palliative care to patients with advanced cancer, pain management is a key consideration. Palliative care aims to improve the quality of life for patients by managing physical, psychological, and emotional symptoms effectively. Pain management is crucial in providing comfort and well-being for those with advanced cancer.

122. A: Sarah's symptoms indicate psychosocial distress, which is common in cancer patients. As an oncology nurse, it is essential to recognize and address these distressing feelings. Providing emotional support is crucial, but it is equally important to refer Sarah to a mental health professional who specializes in counseling cancer patients.

123. C: Cancer treatment can have diverse effects on the sexual health of patients, ranging from physical symptoms such as fatigue, pain, and hormonal changes to emotional and psychological concerns like body image issues and anxiety.

124. D: Anaphylaxis can be triggered by various factors in oncology patients. Contrast media used in imaging studies, particularly iodinated contrast agents, can trigger anaphylactic reactions. Additionally, blood transfusions may lead to transfusion-related acute lung injury (TRALI), which can present with symptoms similar to anaphylaxis. Oncology nurses must be vigilant and aware of these potential triggers to recognize and manage anaphylactic emergencies in their patients promptly.

125. D: The Patient Health Questionnaire (PHQ-9) is a commonly used screening tool for depression in healthcare settings. There are nine questions designed to assess the severity of depressive symptoms in patients.

126. C: Peripheral neuropathy is a common alteration in functioning observed in oncology patients undergoing chemotherapy. Chemotherapy drugs can cause damage to the nerves, leading to symptoms such as numbness, tingling, burning sensation, muscle weakness, and loss of reflexes in the extremities. This can significantly impact the patient's ability to perform fine motor tasks, balance, and coordination.

127. B: Fatigue is a common side effect experienced by patients receiving radiation therapy, and it may persist for several weeks after treatment completion. Skin changes, such as redness and dryness, are also common due to the effect of radiation on the skin. Additionally, urinary problems, such as increased frequency or urgency, may occur. However, it is important to reassure the patient that these side effects are usually temporary and can be effectively managed with various interventions such as medication, skin care measures, and bladder training techniques. It is crucial for the oncology certified nurse to provide accurate information and address the patient's concerns regarding radiation therapy. Incorrect options provide inaccurate and misleading information, which can lead to misconceptions and anxiety for the patient.

128. B: T lymphocytes, also known as T cells, play a vital role in cell-mediated immunity. These cells are responsible for recognizing and attacking infected cells directly.

129. B: "Radiation therapy increases the risk of developing subsequent malignancies in nearby healthy tissues."

130. A: Vaginal dryness and pain during intercourse are common side effects of cancer treatment, particularly hormonal therapies. Over-the-counter vaginal moisturizers are specifically designed to alleviate these symptoms and improve comfort during sexual activity. They help to restore natural moisture and reduce friction.

131. C: Unresolved grief refers to grief that persists for an extended period, interfering with a person's daily life and preventing them from adapting to the loss. One common symptom of unresolved grief is the inability to engage in regular activities, such as work or social interactions. Additionally,

individuals experiencing unresolved grief may lose interest in previously enjoyed hobbies or activities they once found pleasure in.

132. D: According to the scope and standards of oncology nursing practice, it is crucial for the nurse to collaborate and communicate with the oncologist. In this scenario, the nurse should notify Sarah's oncologist about the fever, fatigue, and sore throat. These symptoms may indicate a potential infection, and it is essential to involve the oncologist to determine the appropriate course of action.

133. A: The prognosis of site-specific cancers is influenced by various factors, but tumor size and stage are crucial in determining the outlook for the patient.

134. D: TLS is associated with the release of intracellular contents into the bloodstream..

135. D: Spinal cord compression often presents with back pain as one of the initial symptoms. As the condition progresses, muscle weakness, altered sensation, and bowel or bladder dysfunction may develop.

136. A: Breast cancer commonly spreads to the liver through the bloodstream. Liver metastasis occurs when breast cancer cells break away from the primary tumor and travel to the liver. This is primarily due to the rich blood supply of the liver and its role in filtering and processing blood. Metastasis to the liver can lead to symptoms such as abdominal pain, jaundice, fatigue, and weight loss. Detecting liver metastasis early is crucial for effective treatment and improved outcomes in breast cancer patients.

137. B: During the bereavement process, individuals commonly experience stages of grief. Anger is one of the commonly observed stages, where the person may express frustration, resentment, and hostility. This stage is an important part of the healing process as the person processes their emotions and adjusts to the loss. It is crucial for oncology nurses to recognize and support individuals experiencing anger during bereavement, providing them with appropriate coping mechanisms to navigate this stage of grief.

138. A: One of the common complications associated with the use of vascular access devices (VADs) for treatment administration is catheter dislodgement.

139. B: Altering or falsifying patient records is a serious violation of legal and ethical principles in nursing practice. It compromises patient safety, undermines trust, and is considered a form of misconduct. Nurses should always prioritize accuracy, objectivity, and transparency when documenting patient assessments, interventions, and outcomes. Additionally, maintaining patient confidentiality and using appropriate medical terminology are essential aspects of documentation. Upholding these standards ensures the integrity of the healthcare system and protects both patients and healthcare providers.

140. D: An appropriate nursing intervention to help manage cognitive changes in cancer patients receiving palliative care is to minimize environmental stimuli. Reducing noise, distractions, and excessive visual stimulation can help promote cognitive focus and reduce confusion. Creating a calm and soothing environment can enhance the patient's ability to concentrate and communicate effectively. It is important for the nurse to provide a quiet and peaceful space for the patient, free from unnecessary sensory overload, to support their cognitive functioning.

141. C: Lung cancer commonly metastasizes to the bones, making it a significant site of metastatic spread.

142. D: Hemoptysis (coughing up blood) is not a typical symptom of SVCS. It is more commonly associated with other respiratory conditions, such as lung cancer or bronchitis.

143. C: As an oncology nurse, it is crucial to base your practice on evidence-based research. In this scenario, the nurse's role is to critically appraise and review the current evidence regarding the use of honey dressings for post-operative wound care.

144. A: Neurological alterations in oncology patients can commonly manifest as visual disturbances. These changes can include blurred vision, double

vision, or even loss of vision. These symptoms may be a result of tumor growth or spread of cancer to the brain, side effects of treatment, or paraneoplastic syndromes.

145. C: Active listening involves giving full attention to the speaker, providing verbal and non-verbal cues to show understanding and empathy. By actively listening to Sarah's concerns, the nurse can create a safe and supportive environment, encourage her to express her feelings, and gather important information to address her needs effectively.

146. C: Elevating the head of the bed to 30 degrees helps decrease intracranial pressure by promoting venous outflow and improving cerebral blood flow. This position facilitates drainage and helps prevent additional increases in ICP.

147. A: Advanced care planning is a legal document that outlines the medical treatments a patient wishes to receive or avoid if they become unable to make decisions.

148. C: A high intake of fruits and vegetables is actually associated with a decreased risk of developing cardiovascular diseases. This is because fruits and vegetables contain essential nutrients, vitamins, and antioxidants that help to maintain heart health by reducing inflammation, improving blood pressure, and fighting oxidative stress.

149. B: Chernotherapy drugs can cause a significant impact on the immune system by reducing the production of white blood cells, which are responsible for fighting off infections. This suppression of the immune system increases the risk of infections in cancer patients undergoing treatment.

150. C: Lisa's symptoms of persistent fatigue, difficulty concentrating, and memory problems are consistent with chemobrain, also known as chemotherapy-induced cognitive impairment. Chemobrain is a common long-term side effect of chemotherapy and can impact a patient's quality of life.

151. A: Discrimination concerns can have a significant impact on a patient's overall well-being and quality of care. By educating the healthcare team

about the importance of cultural sensitivity and diversity training, the oncology certified nurse can promote equality and understanding among the staff.

152. C: A patient with altered body image following breast surgery may feel self-conscious, which can lead to decreased self-esteem and confidence. Recommending the use of a prosthetic breast can help restore balance and symmetry, giving the patient a more natural appearance and potentially improving body image.

153. C: A sentinel lymph node biopsy is a procedure commonly performed during breast cancer surgery. It involves identifying and removing the first lymph node(s) where cancer cells are most likely to spread from the primary tumor.

154. C: As an Oncology Certified Nurse, it is essential to understand the legal obligations and professional responsibilities associated with your practice. Therefore, maintaining licensure and complying with state laws and regulations are crucial aspects of legal protection.

155. C: When considering long-term treatment administration, an implanted port is the most appropriate vascular access device. It provides a reliable and low-profile option for repeated access to the vascular system. The port is placed beneath the skin, minimizing the risk of infection and offering a cosmetically appealing option for patients.

156. C: Family and social support have a significant impact on the survivorship and care continuum for individuals affected by cancer.

157. B: Mrs. Johnson's low oxygen saturation indicates a need for supplemental oxygen.

158. A: Collaboration in oncology nursing involves the active participation and exchange of information and ideas between healthcare professionals, including nurses, physicians, pharmacists, and other members of the interdisciplinary team.

159. C: Grief is a normal response to loss, and in the case of Sarah, her diagnosis and prognosis represent a significant loss. It is crucial for the nurse to create a safe and welcoming space where Sarah feels comfortable expressing her emotions.

160. A: The symptoms of sudden onset of shortness of breath, wheezing, and a rash are consistent with a Type I hypersensitivity reaction, also known as immediate hypersensitivity or anaphylactic reaction.

161. A: Quality of practice in oncology nursing is closely linked to adhering to evidence-based guidelines. Evidence-based practice involves integrating the best available research evidence with clinical expertise and patient preferences to make informed decisions and deliver high-quality care.

162. B: Evidence-based practice in oncology nursing involves the integration of individual clinical expertise, patient preferences, and the best available research evidence. It emphasizes a comprehensive approach to patient care, combining the nurse's knowledge and experience with the latest research findings.

163. A: The most appropriate intervention for managing Sarah's symptoms and reducing unnecessary emergency department visits is to educate her about potential side effects and self-management strategies. By equipping Sarah with knowledge about the expected side effects of chemotherapy and strategies to mitigate them, she can proactively manage her symptoms at home, reducing the need for emergency department visits.

164. A: When addressing intimacy with cancer patients, it is crucial to provide education on sexual health resources.

165. B: Government-funded assistance programs such as Medicaid and Medicare provide financial aid to individuals who are unable to afford the cost of their healthcare. These programs often cover the cost of chemotherapy drugs and other cancer treatments for eligible patients.

References

Polit, D. F., & Beck, C. T. (2004). *Nursing research: Principles and methods.* Lippincott Williams & Wilkins.

Crespel, L., & Meynet, J. (2017). Manipulation of Ploidy Level. In Science Direct. https://doi.org/10.1016/b978-0-12-809633-8.05004-4

Jones, M. P. (2020). The Social Determinants of COVID-19. The Journal of the Association of Black Nursing Faculty in Higher Education. https://pesquisa.bvsalud.org/global-literature-on-novel-coronavirus-2019-ncov/resource/en/covidwho-972946

Center to Advance Palliative Care. (n.d.). About palliative care. https://www.capc.org/about/palliative-care

Institute of Medicine. (2014). Dying in America: Improving quality and honoring individual preferences near the end of life: Key findings and recommendations. https://nap.nationalacademies.org/catalog/18748/dying-in-america-improv

National Cancer Institute. (2021). Palliative care in cancer. https://www.cancer.gov/about-cancer/advanced-cancer/care-choices/palliative-care-fact-sheet#:~:text=Palliative%20care%20is%20care%20meant,whole%2C%20not%20just%20their%20disease

National Consensus Project. (2018). Clinical practice guidelines for quality palliative care (4th ed.). https://www.nationalcoalitionhpc.org/wp-content/uploads/2018/10/NCHPC-N

Oncology Nursing Certification Corporation. (2022). OCN® test content outline. https://www.oncc.org/files/2018OCNTestContentOutline.pdf

Oncology Nursing Society. (2022a). Access to quality cancer care [Position statement]. https://ons.org/advocacy-policy/positions/policy/access

Oncology Nursing Society. (2022b). Oncology certification for nurses [Position statement]. https://ons.org/advocacy-policy/positions/education/certification

Vanbutsele, G., Pardon, K., Van Belle, S., Surmont, V., De Laat, M., Colman, R., . . . Deliens, L. (2018). Effect of early and systematic integration of palliative care in patients with advanced cancer: A randomised controlled trial. Lancet Oncology, 19(3), 394-404. https://doi.org/10.1016/s1470-2045(18)30060-3

Made in the USA
Columbia, SC
08 May 2024